The WRAP® Story:
First Person Accounts of Personal and
System Recovery and Transformation

Collected by and with contributions from
Mary Ellen Copeland

Peach Press

Table of Contents

Note from Mary Ellen

This book is a compilation of stories from around the world of people using the Wellness Recovery Action Plan® (WRAP®). I gathered these stories from individual people who are using WRAP; from WRAP group facilitators; from people who are using WRAP in their organizations; and from people who are using WRAP to transform the mental health system in their organization, area, state, region or country. These stories are so personal that I made the decision to leave them largely unchanged and unedited. I left in parts that might seem repetitive or not relevant. Some may be hard to read, hard to understand. But for someone or some people it might be just those words that move them out of despair, give them hope, or share an idea that really works for them. There was no way I could judge that. So they are all here. You can read what it is that you find most useful to you.

The people who wrote these stories gave their all, revisiting difficult times and sharing personal information in the hope that it would be useful and inspire someone else. I am so grateful.

Except for the stories about integrating WRAP into the Mental Health System, I have done my best to make each writer anonymous.

Where WRAP Came From

When I think about where WRAP came from, my thoughts go back in time, much further than I thought they would go. They go back in time to when I was a very little girl, eight years old, lonely and frightened, as a nurse with lots of keys unlocked numerous heavy doors, leading me and my siblings to the large, noisy and scary room where we would have our brief weekly visit with my mother. She had been taken there after she experienced deep and seemingly intractable depression, and after my father had been told that she was incurably insane.

Our visit was brief and impersonal. It was hard to find the woman we remembered as Ma in the midst of multitudes of agitated people pacing, crying, screaming and often interrupting any semblance of a conversation we were trying to have with our mother, who was herself constantly walking in circles and repeating over and over words we couldn't understand. I think WRAP began there, in the mind of a small girl who became convinced that what was happening here was wrong and bad, that there was no chance anyone could get well and stay well in this circumstance, where the only treatment was an occasional barbaric electro-shock treatment (they were really barbaric in the old days, irrespective of how they are viewed today) and an occasional ceramics class.

In spite of all, after eight years in that horrible place, my mother did get well. She came home and gradually, over time, picked up the pieces of her life and moved on. I think at that point, the possibility that people might recover became a little clearer for me. I watched what was happening, and as I look back, wish I had been more supportive, rather than a typical, somewhat difficult teen-ager, away at college and building a life of my own. I saw how she built new, supportive relationships, pursued her long dormant career as a dietician, and worked to maintain her wellness and continue her recovery with too little support from family and none from care providers. What a brave woman!

Through this time I went to college, got married, had a family, and was diverted from that niggling thought in my mind, "People can get over this." But I was a total self help "junkie." I read every self-help book and article I could get my hands on. And, because I was experiencing deep depressions in my own life, I tried the things I learned. And a lot of them helped. Especially relaxation and stress reduction techniques, diet and other "alternative" options. I raised my children, began a career, and life moved along in spite of the depressions and some expansive moods that were becoming almost constant companions. And still the thought lingered in the back of my mind. There is something you can do. People don't need to go through this. I took it out, dusted it off and reviewed it from time to time and then it settled back into its place at the back of my mind.

And then something happened that catapulted that thought into clear view. I had been overworking and leading a very stressful life. I was in a bad marriage and had many more responsibilities than any one person should have. In the process of getting out of the marriage and trying to rebuild my life, my times of deep sadness increased, and also some puzzling times when, for no good reason, I felt absolutely terrific, better than I had ever felt in my life. At times my moods were so expansive and I enjoyed them so much that I failed to notice the ominous signs that were becoming so clear to family members and friends.

My world caved in. The deep despair, and then extreme elation, turned my life into a nightmare. Friends fell by the wayside as I ignored them or treated them badly. I did things I will always regret. I bought things that I didn't need and didn't have the money to pay for. I drove recklessly. I nearly ended my life, both intentionally and inadvertently. I lost my job and had no way to support myself. It seemed like my life was over. I thought my family had given up on me.

After repeated hospitalizations and trials on stronger and stronger medications, I said to my psychiatrist, "How do people like me recover? How do they get well, stay well and get on with their lives?" He said he would get that information for me for the next appointment.

I looked forward to the next appointment with great anticipation. Finally I was going to get some information that would lead me out of this morass. Imagine my disappointment when he told me that there was no information of that kind. He said, "We have information on medication options and on treatment programs, but nothing on how people get well and move on with their lives." I was astounded. And it was then that the thought that had lain dormant in my mind for so long stirred. It said, "You need to talk to people like yourself, people who have all these horrid 'symptoms' and life experiences. You need to ask them what helps. If you get information from enough people, you will be able to figure out what to do for yourself."

I devised a plan to develop a survey and ask people like me to fill it out. I didn't really know the questions. I thought I would make them very open-ended, hoping if people wrote a lot, I could glean some answers, and then perhaps even figure out some new questions from their answers. I thought I could get volunteers by putting short articles in various mental health newsletters.

I went to talk to my vocational rehabilitation counselor about this grandiose scheme, fully expecting a rebuff. After all, I had been living with out-of-control mood swings for quite a long time. Why should anyone have any confidence in me? To my surprise she said, "What a great idea!" Then she proceeded to help me develop a Social Security Plan to Achieve Self Sufficiency that would give me money for a computer, paper and supplies for the surveys, postage and phone money—enough to get me started.

It was slow going at first. I was trying to cope with deep depression, lack of motivation, low self-confidence, anxiety, lethargy and general malaise. But somewhere inside of me there was a spark that kept me going as I set up a working space for myself in my tiny apartment, learned how to use a computer, and developed articles to put in mental health publications to get volunteers. I wasn't ready for the positive response I received. I got hundreds of phone calls and letters (this was before e-mail). I ended up with 125 volunteers, people who said they were willing to respond to a series of open-ended questions that might give me some insights on how people with various kinds of mental health difficulties cope on a daily basis, how they work toward meeting their life goals and what helps them to feel better when they are not feeling well.

My next project was to develop the surveys. I decided I would have three surveys. People could send me back the first one and I could use what I learned to develop the second one and then, in the same way, the third, building each time on what I had discovered through the previous survey. People who did research professionally gave me a really hard time. They said it would never work. Some even made fun of what they said were my primitive attempts at research. They said I would never be able to compile data from the open-ended questions I was using. They said I should ask a question and then get people to rate the answer with a number, 5,4,3,2, or 1, a process I had no interest in at all. I was uninterested because, as I began, I did not even know what questions to ask. I had to develop some questions that were my best guess at what might get people sharing, and then use this sharing to develop questions that were more targeted toward getting useful information.

As it turned out, I got the most information from people writing in the blank space that I left for additional information at the end of each section and at the back of the survey.

What I got back from these surveys was amazing. People were so eager to share. They said no one had ever before asked them for this kind of information. They wrote up the sides and all over the front and back of the survey booklets. Some sent in tape recordings and articles from

5

magazines. As these survey booklets began piling up in my living room, the task that lay ahead seemed insurmountable. How was I to compile this information in a way that made sense or could be helpful to anyone? Gradually I developed a system that seemed to work. I didn't know it at the time, but it was a computer program. And as I input data, I began to see patterns emerge. Things people did to help themselves became clearer and clearer. I learned about support groups, crisis plans, maintaining key relationships, diet, light, exercise and numerous "tricks" that help people feel better. I learned how people managed their medications and their relationships with health care providers. I learned how people made the best of hospital stays and how they did their best to avoid them.

The more information I compiled, the more changes I made in my own life. And I started feeling better and better. Now with new energy and enthusiasm, I set up a couple of workshops to share my findings. A health care provider told me I could never give a workshop, but I did. It was packed and people loved it. The response was so great I held another one, again to a full house. Then I was asked to present at the National Alliance for the Mentally Ill Conference, my first trip since my mental health had been so troublesome. They gave me a small, difficult-to-find room to present in, thinking my subject matter would be of little interest. But the room was jam-packed and people were standing in the hall trying to get in. It was a huge success.

That was a beginning for me. People started asking me to come to their area to lead workshops. To do that, I began to compile the information into a book so I would have something to hand out to participants. The book was so popular that I sent it off to several publishers for possible publication. Some people shook their heads and told me the publishers wouldn't even look at it. But before long a publisher called me and said they wanted to publish the book. I was off and running.

For the next few years I traveled, taught about what I had learned, wrote several more books and had them published, all while continuing to work on my wellness and to rebuild my life. I worked myself off of Social Security and even bought a home of my own.

Then in 1997, something remarkable happened. I was working in northern Vermont with a group of people (most of whom had mental health difficulties), along with some care providers and family members. On the next-to-the-last day of our eight all-day sessions together, a woman stood up and said, "This is all well and good, but I have been in state hospitals across the country and I wouldn't have any idea how to organize these tools and strategies in my life." This sounded like a challenge to me and to one of the other attendees, Jane Winterling. We were traveling to the sessions together and on the next trip Jane described to me a process that she felt might be the answer to this woman's need. We shared it with the people in the group and they loved it. We worked with them to develop and refine it, to make it into something they really felt would work for them. Alan McNabb, who was assisting with facilitation of the group, thought it should be called a Wellness Recovery Action Plan, WRAP.

It sounded great to me so I went home and on a wintry afternoon developed one for myself. And it really moved me to a new level of wellness. I thought it was so good that I decided to share it at a conference where I was leading a workshop. There I was greeted by a group of people, obviously worn from studying chemical drug formulas and looking at brain slides. I apprehensively presented WRAP. They loved it. The response was overwhelmingly positive.

This is how Alan McNabb remembers it:

> WRAP was developed in Bradford, Vermont, February 1997, in response to the need of a group of 40 individuals. This group of people had just gone through one of Mary Ellen's 8 week workshops, which they thought was good information, but they didn't know how to put it into practice in their daily life. Built into that 8-week workshop were two additional sessions to go over these concerns. During those two additional sessions Mary Ellen and Jane Winterling created a structure starting with Daily Maintenance and ending with Crisis Planning. It

broke down the progression from wellness to illness, creating stages that people could follow back to wellness.

Soon after its inception I came up with the name Wellness Recovery Action Plan. I was teaching a Monday afternoon group at a Lebanon, New Hampshire peer support center called "Wellness Recovery Group". I believed the word Recovery was being over-used and that everyone had a right to not only recover but to regain their Wellness. Since the newly designed Plan was based on the Action of using Wellness Tools, the name came quite naturally. Plus, it created the image in my mind of having a "comfortable wrap or shawl."

Alan says,

WRAP has changed my life and chances are it saved my life. I consider it wellness technology, of which I am a product. Before I was symptom-led and now I am self-led. It has given me choice. It has given me freedom. It has given me my life. I see it being applied to people, to communities, to the world. It has built critical mass and is on the verge of explosion where it will touch more lives than we can imagine. It has the ability to change countless lives in endless ways.

After that, whenever I led a workshop or spoke at conferences, people just wanted to know about WRAP. That summer, I wrote the popular red WRAP Book. Revised over the years, the red WRAP book has now sold thousands and thousands and thousands of copies, is translated into many languages, including Spanish, Japanese and Chinese, and has been revised to meet specific needs of people with a dual diagnosis, veterans and people in the military, and even children (WRAP Workbook for Kids). There are WRAP CDs and DVDs and even a software program. I wrote Winning Against Relapse to begin to describe the various ways that WRAP can be used. In addition I developed a curriculum to teach people how to lead

WRAP groups and began holding several WRAP facilitator seminars each year. Since then it has grown and grown and grown.

The Copeland Center for Wellness and Recovery

As the mental health recovery information that I began gathering in the late 1980's became more and more popular and gained wider recognition, I began thinking about how this work could be expanded and spread more quickly, and how it would be carried on, even after my retirement. When WRAP was developed and became so useful to so many, many people working on their recovery, it became even more clear to me that a way must be developed to assure that this work would continue, and that it would not be dependent on any one person to do so.

My first step in this direction was training people to be mental health recovery group and workshop facilitators (New Hampshire, 1996, soon followed by Vermont). I led these early trainings myself. It soon became apparent to me that people from all over the country and all over the world wanted to attend these trainings. The first WRAP trainings, open to anyone who had taken the Correspondence Course that I offered as a prerequisite, were held in 1998. My husband, Ed Anthes, and Alan McNabb were my assistants in these trainings.

These popular trainings were held here in the Brattleboro area several times a year. People came from all over the country, eager to begin mental health recovery and WRAP programs in their agencies and organizations. In addition, Ed and I, and sometimes Alan and others who were rapidly improving their knowledge base and skills, presented workshops around the country in many regions and states. Ed and I spent time teaching people to be facilitators in England, Ireland, Scotland and New Zealand.

There was more and more demand for these trainings. It was getting beyond my capacity to provide them. But of course I didn't want them to stop. Beginning in 2003, Ed and I began meeting with some leaders in the national mental health recovery movement about setting up a non-profit organization that would provide mental health recovery and WRAP training at all levels: for people who wanted basic training; for those who wanted to lead WRAP groups; for those who wanted to teach people how to become group facilitators; and for people who wanted to know how to integrate mental health recovery and WRAP into their mental health system.

In 2005, The Copeland Center for Wellness and Recovery came into being, taking over responsibility for all the Mental Health Recovery and WRAP training activities. It has been going full tilt ever since.

The Center pairs people with a strong grasp of the knowledge base and values and ethics of mental health recovery and WRAP, who have leadership skills and years of experience, with agencies and organizations that request WRAP training. In addition, a strong schedule of training events continues to be held here in Brattleboro, Vermont. At the beginning, I was doing training, still with the help of Ed and Alan. Now that is all being handled by the Copeland Center.

There were two big accomplishments of the Copeland Center that initial year. First was the WRAP Conference, held in July at the University of Massachusetts in Amherst. Three hundred people attended, from all over the world. I gave a keynote address each day, and people attended a wide variety of workshops that included in-depth descriptions of each section of WRAP, the WRAP and mental health recovery values and ethics, various Wellness Tools, and using WRAP in specific circumstances. People are still talking about their experiences there. More conferences like this one are planned in other parts of the country.

The second big accomplishment was hiring an Executive Director, Stephen Pocklington, and a Program Coordinator/Business Manager, Nancy Haldeman, in Fall of that first year. (Before that, several people helped set up the conference and kept the ball rolling.) They both hit the ground running, Stephen in New Bern, North Carolina and Nancy in Chandler, Arizona, communicating and commiserating electronically, and doing it very well. And I must mention Alan McNabb. Although he does his best to steer clear of the administrative details, you will find him working closely with Stephen, trying continually to perfect something that many people already feel is perfect. And that is just what needs to be done.

Since Stephen and Nancy joined the Copeland Center, it has grown exponentially. There are more and more trainings all the time. Seasoned Mental Health Recovery Educators, through a certification process, become eligible to lead Copeland Center-sponsored trainings. Along with Stephen and Alan, these trainers have acquired a reputation for being the best there is. Along with more trainers and more trainings, the variety of training options available is growing. In addition, the Center is often called upon to consult with agencies and organizations that are interested in developing a recovery focus.

Apart from, but working closely with the Center, I continue to do research and coordinate research activities, and to develop new mental health recovery and WRAP resources based on my findings. Ed publishes and distributes all of these resources through Peach Press.

I have the privilege of sitting back, more than I ever have, and watching all of this grow. This center is the greatest memorial I could ever give to my mother, and the many people like her, who spent years of their lives locked up in institutions, told they could never recover, never offered any Wellness Tools.

The exciting thing about this work is the stories I hear about how WRAP, and the values and ethics that have evolved from it, have affected, transformed and even saved people's lives, and how it has done the same thing for people who teach others about WRAP and even for the mental health system. This is a book of some of those stories.

These stories were collected through requests sent out through The Copeland Center for Wellness and Recovery newsletter lists. In addition, I sent specific requests to people who I felt had stories that I wanted to share with you.

But before we get into stories, you may be asking, "What is WRAP?" The next chapter will focus on that.

What is WRAP®- the Wellness Recovery Action Plan®?

Now that you know how WRAP was developed, you may be wondering what exactly WRAP is.

WRAP is a self-designed plan for staying well, and for helping you to feel better when you are not feeling well, to increase personal responsibility and control over your own life, and help you make your life the way you want it to be. Many people like to develop it in a three ring binder with tabs. However, other kinds of notebooks can be used. Some people tape record their plan and some have used pictures instead of words. There are no hard and fast rules around WRAP except that WRAP has to be developed by the person who is going to use it. It can't be developed by someone else. If it is, it's not WRAP.

The first part of WRAP is developing a personal *Wellness Toolbox*. This is a list of things you can use to develop your WRAP. It includes actions like contacting friends and supporters, peer counseling, focusing exercises, relaxation and stress reduction exercises, journaling, doing a creative, fun and affirming activity, exercising, diet, light, and getting a good night's sleep. It can be a long or a short list. Many people find that at first their list is short, but over time, as they have more experience, they discover many more Wellness Tools. I used to have just a few things on my list. Now I have over 80. I have come to realize that things like petting my dog, taking a break, or even working, can be Wellness Tools, depending on when I use them.

🐦

Section 1 of WRAP is the *Daily Maintenance Plan*. It includes the following three parts:

1. A description of yourself when you are well. This serves as a reminder when you have been feeling not well for some time and forget what feeling well is like. It also keeps you in touch with what you want to feel like, what you are working toward. It might include words like happy, optimistic, introverted, quiet or cantankerous.

2. The Wellness Tools you know you must use every day to maintain your wellness, like getting a half hour of exercise, drinking 8 glasses of water and doing something fun.

3. A list of things you might need to do on any day (you can add in things you do weekly, monthly or even every year if you want to). This part of the plan was very important to me. I came to realize that if I was sure to do certain things each day, like paying my bills, getting some groceries or checking in with my family, I really felt quite good. And if I got "off track," I noticed the difference right away.

Section 2 is identifying those events or *Triggers* that, if they happened, might make you feel worse—like an argument with a friend or getting a big bill. Then, using Wellness Tools, you develop an action plan you can use to get through this difficult time. On my Triggers Action Plan, I have included lots of options, because you never know when you might be triggered, and what might be possible to do at that time. One of the ones I use most often is, if something unexpected that is difficult happens, I find a quiet space and spend a few minutes putting myself together and deciding what to do next. Then I often talk to someone about what has happened and figure out, what, if any, next steps I have to take.

Section 3 is identifying *Early Warning Signs*, those subtle signs that let you know you are beginning to feel worse, like being unable to sleep or feelings of nervousness. Signs that I noticed for me were that I stop

13

buckling my seat belt and am careless about watching for traffic when I cross the street. Next, again using your Wellness Toolbox, develop an action plan for responding to these signs so that you feel better quickly and prevent a possible more difficult time. When I notice early warning signs, I try to take a two-hour break to do one of my favorite things, like going for a long walk or doing some kind of artwork or quilting. If I don't feel better after that, I take more time the next day to do fun things on my Wellness Tool list. That always works for me.

Section 4 is *When Things are Breaking Down*. In this section, you list those signs that let you know you are feeling much worse, like you are feeling extremely sad all the time. Next, list the Wellness Tools that can help you feel better as quickly as possible and prevent an even more difficult time. When this happens to me I use the plans I have developed for at least three days. These plans include visits to my counselor, time with friends, good food, exercise, time outdoors, lots of time listing to music I love and doing those things I enjoy. This works for me. I haven't been hospitalized in many years.

Section 5 is a *Crisis Plan* or *Advance Directive*. In the crisis plan, you identify: those signs that let others know they need to take over responsibility for your care and decision making (like substance abuse, being abusive to others, or certain compulsive behaviors); who you want to take over for you and support you through this time; health care in-formation; a plan for staying at home through this time if at all possible; things others can do that would help; and things they might choose to do that would not be helpful. This kind of proactive advance planning keeps you in control even when it seems like things are out of control. You give copies of this part of the plan to all those people you listed as supporters so they know just what to do. Supporters love these plans.

Section 6 is the *Post Crisis Plan*. This part of the plan deals with that difficult time right after you have had a crisis, when you are trying to heal and get back to feeling good again. You may want to think about this part of the plan in advance and even write some things to do in that time. However, you may want to write most of it as you are beginning to recover from the crisis—when you have a clearer picture of what you need to do for yourself to get well.

ॐ

Review your plans every day, noting how you feel and doing what you need to do to help yourself get better or to keep yourself well. As you become familiar with your plan, you will find that the review process takes less time and that you will know how to respond without even referring to the book. People who are using these plans regularly, and updating them as necessary, are finding that they have fewer difficult times, and that when they do have a hard time it is not as bad as it used to be and it doesn't last as long. It is certainly true of me. This plan has literally changed and saved my life. Many others report the same thing.

The WRAP approach empowers you to take control of your own health and wellness. Since its development, the system has been shared with thousands of people through the books Wellness Recovery Action Plan, Winning Against Relapse, the WRAP Step-by-Step Audio cd, the Creating Wellness Video series, numerous support groups, workshops and seminars, and through the www.mentalhealthrecovery.com web site.

Most people learn about WRAP in small, informal groups sponsored by mental health agencies or organizations. This seems to work best, as people in these groups learn so much from each other. WRAP facilitators usually lead these groups. These facilitators can be trained through The Copeland Center for Wellness and Recovery.

Having a certified WRAP facilitator assures that the values and ethics of WRAP will be followed. These values and ethics have grown up around WRAP over time. People agree that they are critical to personal success for people in WRAP-based programs, and even in working on them with a supporter.

An abbreviated and adapted listing of the values and ethics follows (for a more complete listing, go to the website www.mentalhealthrecovery.com):

    ❦   WRAP supports the premise that there is hope, that people can get well, stay well for long periods of time, and do the things they want to do with their lives.

- Self-determination, personal responsibility, empowerment, and self-advocacy are key aspects of all WRAP activities.
- WRAP supports group decision-making and personal sharing.
- All people who work on WRAP are equals and must be treated at all times with dignity, compassion, mutual respect, and unconditional high regard.
- There is unconditional acceptance of everyone as they are: unique, special individuals, including acceptance of diversity with relation to culture, ethnicity, language, religion, race, gender, age, disability, sexual preference, and "readiness" issues.
- In WRAP, there are "no limits" to recovery.
- WRAP encourages people to explore choices and options, and does not provide simple, final answers.
- All participation in WRAP-related activities is voluntary.
- It is understood that each person is the expert on her or himself.
- The focus is on individual strengths and away from perceived deficits.
- Clinical, medical and diagnostic language is not used in WRAP
- The focus is on peers working together and learning from each other to increase mutual understanding, knowledge and to promote wellness.
- WRAP emphasizes strategies that are simple and safe for anyone, and de-emphasizes strategies that may have harmful effects.
- Difficult feelings and behaviors are seen as normal responses to traumatic circumstances and in the context of what is happening and not as symptoms or a diagnosis.

Now we will move on to the real substance of this book, the WRAP stories from around the country and around the world.

WRAP Stories

Many, many people, as individuals, like me, have developed Wellness Recovery Action Plans. However, in all the years that I have been spreading the word about WRAP, I have found that no two people have the same story of how they developed their WRAP and how they use it in their lives. The following are mostly unabridged and minimally edited versions of their WRAP life stories. The reason I chose to leave them exactly as they were sent to me is because I don't know what piece of information, vignette or word might be important to you or even change your life. So it's all here. If some stories don't interest you that much, or you find parts are boring, go on to the next story, knowing that the story you skipped over might absolutely meet the needs of someone else.

Some of the stories contain medical and other language that I do not usually use. But I have included it here. These stories do not belong to me, but rather to the people who have written them.

1

I was hospitalized in 1993, 2000, and 2003. Each time was because of manic episodes. Since my first visit I have had many labels, schizophrenic, bi-polar — sometimes it was bi-polar I, sometimes bi-polar II. There have been other labels as well, but I've never paid attention to them. The label has always depended on whom I saw, when I saw them, what was going on in my life, and where I was in my mood cycle. I knew since my first visit to the hospital something was wrong. When you think the CBS logo is the eye of God and everything on that channel has a special message just for you, it's hard to deny there's a problem. I never cared what it was called. I only cared about how it affected my life and what I could do about it.

I always explain my experience of bi-polar as being like that game Cliff Hanger on The Price is Right. When the price guessed is too low and the mountain climber can barely finish the note he's yodeling—every step is a huge effort—that's depression. Stability would be when you guess the correct price. Hypomania would be when the price guessed is too high and I'm racing up the mountain. Then comes full-blown mania when I am floating around in outer space with my delusions and hallucinations. Eventually I quit floating around in my special version of reality and crash into depression. I never bother going back down the mountain the way I came — I just jump off and crash. Then I lie there and vegetate in my coma. My mom died young and I'm a single mother. Because of this I never once considered suicide. I know I'm fortunate to have my son—he gives my life a sense of purpose. So, eventually I crawl to the bottom of the mountain and try again.

Before I found out about WRAP this seemed like a never-ending cycle that I had little or no control over. I didn't even get to guess the price. I was told that medication would control things. It didn't—often it just added to my problems. When I complained about the problems I was told I was "in denial" or I "just liked being manic." I knew this wasn't true. I felt frustrated and misunderstood. I didn't think my doctors were listening to me so I didn't want to listen to them. So they gave me a new label—non-compliant. I knew I was in trouble. I knew I needed help. I knew my doctors were nice people with good intentions, but I wasn't getting the help I needed.

Shortly before my third visit to the hospital I started to read everything I could find that was written by people who actually had bi-polar. At the time I had a really good therapist, who unfortunately moved away a month after I got out of the hospital. I really liked her because she gave me homework and suggested books for me to read. When I first began to see her I was in a deep depression. She had me make a list of things that I used to enjoy doing. Then she encouraged me to try to start doing things on that list. I did what she suggested and I started to come out of my depression. So she got me to start crawling out of my depression, then I started walking, until once again I was running and racing up the mountain. This is when my therapist said to me "I'm probably going to regret this, but you should read this book called *The Depression Workbook*— it was written by a woman who has bi-polar disorder. She sent out questionnaires to other people who have bi-polar and used that information to write this book." This is when I was introduced to Mary Ellen Copeland's work for the first time.

When I read this book it made sense to me. I could feel in my gut it was true because the things in the book matched my personal experiences. The first thing that struck me was learning that if you recognized you were in trouble and took action quickly, then your symptoms would not be as severe. I don't know what this says about my friends and family, but nobody noticed I was in trouble the first time. I was in severe psychosis for a full month before someone finally brought me to the hospital. The person who called 911 was someone I barely knew. The next time I went to the hospital after only 1 week of being in trouble. The difference between my state of mind the first time I entered the hospital when compared to the second and third time is extreme. The month before my first visit I didn't sleep or eat for a month. I lost 40 pounds that month, which was nice, but it's not a diet I recommend. I had hallucinations and delusions all three times that I was hospitalized, but the first time was much more severe and lasted a lot longer than the other two. The other thing that I knew was effective was creating and using a Wellness Toolbox. That isn't what my therapist called it when she had me make my list, but I recognized it when I read about it and knew that it worked.

During my frantic, manic reading spree, another book I read was a biography about Vincent Van Gogh. During his life he discovered that certain people and places were "triggers" and when he avoided them he didn't have as many problems with his mental health. This only reinforced what I had learned about WRAP.

I was already in the "things were breaking down" stage when I was introduced to this book. A few months later my aunt died. I managed to maintain my instability for two more months before I entered the "crisis" stage and was hospitalized. I'll avoid telling war stories and skip ahead to the part where I regained control of my life and started working my WRAP.

The first and most difficult step I took was looking at my commitments and admitting to myself that I was trying to do too much. What was even harder was admitting that at that moment everything was too much. I finally realized that when I overextend and over-commit myself I get into trouble. This was a brand new concept for me. Before this I always thought that if I had a problem I had to do something about it. It never occurred to me that the solution was to do nothing, not something. I was tired of tackling the same old mountain and if I wanted things to change I needed to give it a rest. Things had reached the point where I had to take a time out from my life and use that time to educate myself about me.

So for the last two years that is what I have been doing. Last spring I was struggling with depression so I tried one of the suggestions in the book and started my very first garden. I'm still surprised at how much better it made me feel. My son made fun of me because I would make everyone who stopped by rub the leaves of my lavender and mint plants and smell their fingers. I took time to "smell the lavender" several times a day. Another suggestion I took was to do something special for myself on days that were typically hard. I started buying myself flowers on the anniversary of the days my mom and aunt died. I also do this on their birthdays. Having flowers in the house just seems to make me feel better. The most effective skill that I have been learning (and hope to keep improving) is just recognizing the "early warning signs" as they come up. I monitor my moods closely and adjust my activity and commitments accordingly. If I am overwhelmed and becoming over stimulated, I have learned to take the steps necessary to slow down or stop. When that means I need to stay home and avoid people and places, I do. When I'm under-whelmed and under-stimulated I try to do more. I went back to college last fall, but I only go part-time and I won't take Spring/Summer classes because they are more intense.

My little mountain man still speeds up and slows down. I still don't get to pick the price and it's not always right. But that's okay, because life isn't supposed to be predictable and that's what makes it interesting. What WRAP has done for me is give me a leash for my mountain man. When he is crawling I pull him along. When he starts racing up the mountain I rein him in. The last time I flew off the mountain WRAP was the rope I hung onto. The part that makes me sad is that the mental health system that I have available in my community did more to get in the way of wellness than it did to help me reach stability and maintain it. I would like to be able to trust the hospital that is supposed to help me. I became a recovery facilitator in February 2006 and I sincerely hope things will change. If they do not, it won't be for lack of effort on my part. ॐ

2

I wasn't diagnosed with bipolar until the fall of 2003. Until then I never knew anything was wrong. I knew there were things I had done that I wasn't proud of, and I knew that there were things I did that I couldn't control. I never imagined a lot of it wasn't my fault.

I have never had good coping skills and being on medicine for bipolar didn't help much. Everyone thought if I was on medicine then I would be fine. I thought so also…until I found WRAP.

Before I knew it I was writing poetry again. I had always had to be depressed before I could write. During the WRAP seminar, I wrote fourteen new poems. I met new people and found that I am not alone in this world.

I am still very sick but thanks to WRAP, there is finally a light at the end of my tunnel. I now have a chance of being able to live a somewhat "normal" life. Most people have asked me how a book could help me so much. I tell them that knowledge is power. The more I know about myself and my condition, the better I can care for myself, and those around me don't have to feel helpless if something does go wrong. ❧

3

I am currently in the recovery phase of my mental illness. I have been fighting to get my mental health symptoms under better control for over 14 years. I also have some other disabilities. One being epilepsy, and the other being legal blindness (without glasses, that is).

It was only about a year and half ago that I decided I did not want to be just another mental health statistic. I didn't want to be a label for the rest of my life. I had to take an active role in my own treatment and re-covery. I wanted to move beyond mental illness. I had been to countless doctors and clinics, each giving me a different mental health diagnosis, and putting me on different medications. Some of which worked a little, some not at all. But regardless of what medication I was on, I always had a lot of unwanted side effects. I just had to find an alternative method of controlling symptoms. That's when I found WRAP, "Wellness Recovery Action Plan." I think I had first heard of WRAP back in 2003. From the very start of taking the WRAP class at the behavioral health facility where I receive treatment, I knew it was something that could definitely help me in my recovery.

It was only after developing my WRAP plan, especially figuring out exactly what triggered my symptoms, and then telling my doctor what I'm like when my symptoms are at their worst, compared to what I'm like when I'm symptom free, that an accurate mental health diagnosis was finally made for me. For the first time in my life, I actually agreed with the diagnosis, which turned out to be Adult ADHD with anxiety.

I have made it a weekly habit to review my WRAP, sometimes twice a week if I'm having an extremely tense or stressful week. I want to make sure that I am doing everything in my power to keep myself mentally stable. My mental health has been pretty much unwavering for a little over two years now, thanks to my WRAP plan. I used to end up in psychiatric hospitals (as an inpatient) at least two to five times per year. Now I can honestly say I've only been hospitalized once in the past two and a half years. I was also a very negative person who used to do a lot of acting out. Partly because I was so frustrated with not having much control over my symptoms and partly in order to get some much needed attention. But thanks to WRAP, those behaviors are all behind me now.

WRAP has played an important part in my life. It has helped me to figure out what exactly triggers my anxiety and other mental health symptoms. I have also learned the appropriate tools to use to prevent myself from getting triggered. I now know what to do when things are at the breaking point, when I feel like I'm ready to snap.

I don't know where I would be today had I not found WRAP when I did. With the many trials that I've been through over the past twelve to 15 years, let alone the issues that I have to face today, I probably would have committed suicide by now. The changes in my attitude and my whole outlook on life in general are truly amazing. Even friends and acquaintances of mine have seen the positive changes in my behavior, attitude, and overall well-being. They come up to me all the time just to compliment or congratulate me on the improvement in my mental health and socialization skills.

I believe that psychiatrists, psychologists, and other mental health professionals can be a big help to consumers. But they can't do it all, they are not miracle workers. For me, there were certain symptoms that medication just could not control, or at least could not control without giving me so many unwanted or intolerable side effects. I do a better job controlling most of my symptoms with my WRAP. Besides, no medication in the world can tell me what triggers my symptoms; or help me deal with such triggers in such a positive way as WRAP has.

One of my goals is to someday help my husband develop his own WRAP plan, when he's ready, of course. I would also like to encourage every mental health consumer to develop a WRAP plan for themselves. I think every mental health agency should offer a WRAP class to its consumers. Because if it can help me, I believe it can help anybody. I have accomplished so much over the past two years thanks to WRAP. I am a published writer, I am a full-time college student; pursuing my psychology degree. I am an actress in a local theater company, The Invisible Village Theater, which is a headed by the man who started the Wellness program at Mercy Behavioral Health here in Pittsburgh. I am finally able to go to work. I now work part-time for Mercy Behavioral Health. Best of all, I am better able to handle the stress that comes into my life each day.

I am so grateful for the opportunity I was given by the staff of Mercy Behavioral Health to learn about WRAP. It has been such a life-saving tool in helping me cope with mental health symptoms and dealing with the stigma that comes with having mental illness. I wrote the following poem a couple of years ago to help me in my recovery. It has been published in "Choices-in-Recovery," the Spring 2006 issue:

RECOVERY

November 10, 2004
Dedicated to Mental Health Consumers across this country and beyond who strive everyday to overcome their illnesses.
Recovery can be a lifelong journey on a road full of twists and bends.
Sometimes it can seem as though the journey never ends.
The world may tell us we cannot do it.
They may even put us down.
But if we believe in the abilities within us,
Our true colors in time will be shown.
What we need to do is keep on trucking and never look behind.
For if we focus on the road ahead, our recovery we will find. ❧

4

On the cover of my WRAP (Wellness Recovery Action Plan) Toolbox I have a photograph of myself as a 17 year old U.S. Marine. *Semper Fidelis* (Always Faithful) is the motto of the Corps. That Marines have lived up to this motto is proved by the fact that there has never been a mutiny, or even the thought of one, among U.S. Marines. And I still try to hold this motto twenty-nine years later in applying WRAP to my life – *Semper Fidelis*—and that means being faithful to my life and managing my bipolar disorder in a positive way. WRAP has allowed me to do this. Although I have faithfully kept a written journal since I was about sixteen years young—I can only find journals that go back about twenty-six years, hey, who knew self-care.

I was first diagnosed with bipolar disorder in September 1984 and was placed on a medication regime. I had no idea that there were any support groups, organizations that provided information, and most of the people I encountered who were not diagnosed pretty much indicated "get over it... everybody gets depressed." I thought pushing around furniture every other day, and not needing much sleep, having racing thoughts, and spending money I really did not have, was normal. Then I went the other way – I stopped the medication – and my life crashed. I lost my job, I lost my housing, I lost my significant other, and I decided life was not worth living. Self-medicating probably did not help either. At twenty-six years old I attempted suicide for the fourth time in my life. Yes, I had a suicide plan. The police found me on a beach and I learned later that had they been fifteen minutes later, I would not be here to share my story. I still have a suicide plan, however it is more manageable because I have something I did not have twenty years ago…I have five supports. I try to call them whenever I can and email and visit. However, I am still working on revealing things and definitely if I decide to use my plan I probably will not call. I am still working on my personal crisis plan and advance directives.

My Daily Maintenance List has not changed much since I was about fifteen years old – I clean the house or spot where I am living (some others in my life feel I am obsessive-compulsive about this) and when I am really motivated you get a clean house too. A trigger for me is dirty dishes in the sink and rings around the toilet and shower. I have one friend who constantly leaves dishes in the sink and every time I visit I end up cleaning those dishes and sometimes the whole kitchen (which means refrigerator—laboratory tests get thrown out) She really gets annoyed with this. However, after about twenty-six years of knowing her she should understand it is one of my things. Besides it helps her out. I have another friend whose husband loves to see me. He says "between my obsessive-compulsive and his wife's obsessive-compulsive we make a normal person." I still make my bed up when I get out of bed and it is Marine Corps regulation, bounce-a-quarter made. Although I gave the footlocker up a few years ago I still have one, just not at the end of my rack (that is a bed for you non-military types).

My Daily Maintenance list is fairly long, however, some of my goals and dreams are very important to my personal recovery. One goal I have is that someday I will own a house on a sunny beach. My dream is to have that house in the state of Hawaii. In reality I will most likely have a mobile home by a pond. Where, I am not sure.

Now, I had a really easy time with triggers in my life and probably the biggest trigger is financial concerns. I am on a fixed income and trying to budget the meager amount I receive every month is not easy – thank goodness there are dollar stores everywhere.

I completed my WRAP Certificate of Achievement in 2005, which is a little over a year ago, and I attempt to work in my toolbox at least three times a month. I am still working on the five key concepts to recovery (Hope, Personal Responsibility, Education, Self-Advocacy and Support).

I have some support. However, it really bothers me to bother them when I know they are having concerns of their own and do not need my baggage to go with theirs. Besides, many of them work and are almost impossible to get a hold of.

To me Hope means that I will see another day and have at least one positive thing happen. I was homeless not too long ago and hitchhiking through a town. A young teenager walking by inquired as to where I was going and I explained I was taking a break and trying to locate a mission where I could get something to eat. That same teenager came back about half an hour later and brought me two sandwiches and a Dr. Pepper.

That was a positive thing for me especially coming from the younger generation.

I am still working on Self-Advocacy for myself. Being on disability limits me in so many ways and then the stigma or labels attached to being disabled. I was on public transportation the other day and a person across from me indicated I needed to get up and give my seat to the person who had a cane. I responded not so nice. I pulled out my disability identification, well, I did not assert myself calmly. Could you say that may be a trigger?

I kept thinking how I wanted to conclude this, and a few things have happened this week. I faithfully keep a journal. It is probably one of the consistent things in my life. I actually picked up the telephone and called one person on my support list and two others that probably need to be there. They were shocked because my character and habits – I do not do this. Anyway, I got some very good advice. To them, thank you.

In my life I get really busy, however, I took some time to go see one of my younger friends. Her name is Morganne and she is into dance. She is 11 years wise and has worked very hard for where she is. I am so proud of her and the other members of her dance team. I took dance as a teen (yes, I took ballet for three years and if you mention that, I have plausible deniability). My mother was a dance instructor. 🐾

5

I first heard about the WRAP/Wellness Recovery Action Plan at a conference. The presenter left a contact number to obtain free booklets on the WRAP and other topics. The books were very informative and helped me put a very rough plan into place. I gave the plan to my case manager and also showed it to my clubhouse director. He was impressed and mass ordered copies for the entire clubhouse.

Things were put on hold for a while. Even though I did use portions of the plan, I did not use it daily, but pulled it out for use as necessary.

Our Center for Independent Living sent five people to be trained in Vermont under Mary Ellen Copeland. They in turn trained small groups in which I was able to refine my original plan. I later had the opportunity to also go to Vermont for this same training.

It was an awesome experience. I loved the change of scenery and meeting so many new people. In our group we even had a woman from Alaska. Everyone was very friendly and quickly became a cohesive working team. The sessions were intense but there was time for relaxation. I enjoyed massage therapy while others chose to ski or walk.

Each section was thoroughly gone over. We had to learn to think on our feet, as we had to present both in break out sessions and large group. Our first question in small group was on defending the necessity of recovery in the mental health system and was timed. It was quite daunting in the beginning and then I began to enjoy thinking, sharing ideas, and expecting feedback. I liked this because it gave opportunities to capitalize on my strengths and pointed out where improvements were necessary. It left me with a sense of being listened to, respected, and left me with a sense of hope.

I have found that this plan is continually changing and progressing as I evolve in my growth process. It's never the same nor do I use everything listed. I do not use it on a daily basis. I like knowing it's there when I need it.

The plan was important in that it provided a vision of potential possibilities while offering a sense of hope. I wrote it with those things that I valued and was not what everyone else would've chosen for my recovery journey.

I started off with the Wellness Toolbox. These were activities I had done in the past, had an interest in, or am doing currently. I did struggle with some pain that I didn't realize I still held inside. When I recognized the symptoms and ended up with a diagnosis, I ended all of the old familiar ties to people and events that I once enjoyed.

The Daily Maintenance section was just a list of suggested things I did on a daily basis. I still struggle with this, as some things are done on automatic pilot such as hygiene, grooming, eating, etc. Others were constantly changing, depending upon my health and state of mind at the time. I have to pick and choose my battles. Is it more important that I get out of the apartment and lose the trapped feeling, or stay home and make sure all my chores and my personal upkeep is done for the day? Sometimes you don't win because you either get stigmatized by society, busted by the darn inspections, or by people who stop by to visit, and criticize rather than asking if there's anything you need help with.

Identifying Triggers was very challenging. Me, put down on paper what I consider made me weak, flawed, or vulnerable?! I don't like putting a name on those things that made me feel that way. It was very terrifying and I didn't feel emotionally safe, or confident that this information wouldn't boomerang on me with serious repercussions.

The next section on Early Warning Signs was also a first time step for me. I had never really sat down to individually identify them. I just moved in a blur from A-Z, healthy to hospitalization. Go straight to hell and do not collect $200. There were no intervention techniques to prevent hospitalizations. I continually fell through the cracks in the system. When I thought about it consciously for the first time, there did seem to be familiar patterns to my behaviors and symptoms.

The action plan was to inform my mom and a few close friends to watch for these things. They included poor hygiene, not eating, not talking, failure to show up for scheduled events, and isolating. I was also headachy, irritable, rude, and things became all about me. My world was narrowed down to me and anything or anyone outside of it was meaningless. I always accepted the unconditional love and support of my cat, Smokey, otherwise suspicions and paranoia ran rampant.

Frequently, I get overly dependent on my folks or a friend. I expect them to leave or abandon me so I drive them away by calling them all the time or expecting them to carry me through the rough times. Life doesn't work that way, I lost my best friend of over twelve years. As I am writing this, I should have my folks make me a tape with their voices so I can play it anytime I start getting disconnected. Good idea!

Changes for the good began to occur once things were identified, an awareness developed, and I'm finally learning to ask for help. This helped me to recognize the next stage of When Things Are Breaking Down.

When I noticed or people brought to my attention different things, some insight seemed to appear and I could put some safety nets into place. These were practical, affordable, safe, and healthy things. During this time I had to be honest with myself and do the things I could for myself. I needed to build a trustworthy support network that I could rely on for authentic help.

The Crisis Plan has been rewritten so many times and needs to be changed again as there are new people in my life and different circumstances.

Out of the training I learned I could stay in my own home with supports. This would be great as I'm no longer a threat to myself.

I have used these tools and I feel it's kept me out of the hospital on more than one occasion. I don't want the hospital to be my first and only choice. The hospital should only be used as a last resort. ॐ

6
A Life that has been Rekindled by WRAP

In all probability, in 2004 my inner fire was flickering. At times it was difficult to detect that it was even burning because of my diagnoses, reoccurring hospitalizations, and low self-esteem. In spite of this, I was still reaching out to find answers to my struggles with my mental illness and the impact it was having on my life and the lives of my loved ones. As a result, I agreed to enroll in an educational recovery class, WRAP, which was being offered by my local Mental Health and Recovery Board. A quote written by Albert Schweitzer summarizes the impact the WRAP training session had on my life: "In everyone's life, at sometime, our inner fire goes out. It is then burst into flame by an encounter with another human being. We should all be thankful for those people who rekindle the inner spirit."

My inner spirit was rekindled by this WRAP training session as well as my self-empowerment to work on my diagnoses, reoccurring hospitalizations, and low self-esteem. WRAP training started a flame within me and I will always be thankful for the people like Mary Ellen Copeland and Master WRAP trainers Walter and Carol, who have rekindled my inner spirit. Up to the present time, I have completed my personal WRAP plan, taken the WRAP Educator classes, and am currently involved in teaching others WRAP.

To begin with, I was diagnosed with reoccurring major depression at the age of fifty. In all probability, I started the way down the road to mental illness shortly after I had to quit a job I loved, due to a physical health problem. As a result, I became very depressed. My depression impacted my life in many ways. For example, I was no longer the fun loving, confident person I used to be. Doubtlessly, it was very difficult for my loved ones to know who I was. Likewise, I didn't know who I was either. I had lost my self-worth and identity. At the same time, there was one thing I did know and that was that inside me my heart was breaking. To a great extent, my diagnosis had become a part of my life that was impacting not only my life but also the lives of my loved ones.

Secondly, I had a very high stress level. Certainly, my inability to handle stress and the changes that were occurring in my life led to reoccurring hospitalizations for my major depressive disorder. For instance, my husband and I moved in with our son and his family to assist them. Our son at that time was driving truck and our daughter-in-law was working nights and they needed someone to care for their children while they were working. Needless to say, I took on a very strenuous task of being caregiver, housekeeper, and cook in addition to other obligations that were already on my plate. I would become overwhelmed by feeling as though my husband and I had full responsibility for the household and my illness would escalate. I would end in the hospital, feeling that I had failed and had no reason to live. Naturally, being hospitalized repeatedly lessened my hopes of ever achieving recovery from these reoccurring struggles with my illness.

As a result of this downward spiral in my life, my self-esteem reached an all time low. I continued to search for changes that I thought might help me regain control of my life and illness. For example, my husband and I moved to Elope, Ohio in hopes that things would improve. However, things did not get better for me. The move added to my stress levels because of my constant concern for the care and well being of the grandchildren and my husband's bouts with drinking. I considered my inabilities to meet the needs of everyone else as personal failures, which continually added to my low self-esteem. My self-esteem would reach such a low level that I could see no need of continuing on with life. Even though these life struggles had proven difficult for me, the most difficult struggle came when my husband was diagnosed with terminal cancer. I was able to stay strong to care for him. He was the love of my life despite our ups and downs. I was very saddened by his death in 2004 and was hospitalized twice that following year.

By developing and working with my WRAP, I have not been hospitalized for two years. Developing and using my WRAP has given me back my self-esteem, and sense of pride, and I now have great hope in continuing my recovery. Once again I have found the self-worth and identity that I used to have.

In the final analysis of my recovery journey I can state that my inner fire was burst into flame by my encounter with people who shared the principles of WRAP with me, which has empowered me with hope, a plan for living well, and a plan for maintaining my recovery. My life is more than my diagnoses, reoccurring hospitalizations, and continuous battles of low self-esteem. I will always be thankful for Mary Ellen Copeland and Trainers Walter and Carol, who rekindled my inner spirit. In addition, I am teaching WRAP to others in hopes that someone else's inner spirit will also be rekindled as they develop and work their WRAP plan.

Following is a personal quote:

"I am a survivor, I am a brave warrior, fighting against an illness that can't be seen. But I will keep battling this illness."

7

I talk from the point of view of a client who has essentially been institutionalized via outpatient, inpatient care. For me, this was a necessary viewpoint because I could not picture coping alone, with no other person to tell me what to do. I could not encourage myself, I had to picture/visualize someone beside me through the whole visualization, process, step-by-step. Eventually this unforeseen coping mechanism clicked, and after a good while, I found I could do the coping by myself, visualization or no, mental companion or not. My friends and family have been astonished at how well I am doing now. Good times, bad times, they come and go. I stay in the present reality, and out of the hospital. Plus I laugh a lot more these days. Also, I now have a part-time job, and bought a home.

This is an outline of what my life has been like in terms of coping:

My History

Abuse: physical, sexual, emotional

Many, many, many hospitalizations

Diagnosis

Schizoaffective Disorder, Post Traumatic Stress Disorder

Symptoms

Hallucinations	Suicidal desires	Panic attacks
Dissociation	Psychotic episodes	Mania
Flashbacks	General overwhelming fear	

Skills I learned but could not put into practice on my own

Being alone   Helping myself

Getting out of a bad space without someone telling me what to do.

How I learned to cope on my own

Visualization: I imagine coping with a raging river by using tools such as sandbags, things to build a new ditch for the river, and pair it with things that make me feel better—medicine, phone number/someone to call, calming music, drawing a bubble bath, something to make me laugh, or something to do for someone else.

With each step to take care of river, I take another step to take care of panic. Nothing happens all at once, I would get overwhelmed and panic again. When the river is done, I am coping again. Also, I question and answer journal, writing about my emotions. My heart comes easy, but I don't think other people might find it so.

Now I laugh more, have many friends. I have not been in the hospital once since 2004. I do many more exciting stressful things. I write poetry about mental illness, life, joyful things, and perform or read them to an audience every month, sometimes more. I am on the board of directors of a small non-profit where I will be learning fundraising and public speaking. I work in a non-profit law firm, talking frequently to the public. ॐ

8

WRAP has given me the framework to see the bigger picture. It not only equips me to build my emotional and mental well being, but also to deal with my chronic physical condition. I have built wellness tools into my everyday life— they have become part of the fabric of my life. I don't feel guilty about taking self-time for Wellness Tools. I now feel obliged to create and maintain my mental well-being. I ask myself, "Do you want to be healthy? Do you want to be alive?" Of course I want to be alive, and I also want to be well. I am in control of my WRAP, but I am not alone in achieving it. In my WRAP class, we each build up to five supporters in our life. Right now for me that includes my family, friends, SRG Network, direct payment worker and college support services.

I like the reciprocity that comes with WRAP; my supporters help me to help myself and vice versa. Before WRAP I would not have asked anyone for help. Now if I need help I ask for it. I have realized no one can 'do life' on their own. WRAP has given me a range of new constructs and ways of living.

In activating WRAP, I've had to bite the bullet and address some things I'd rather not have had to address. It's hard work, but it was my decision and I figured if I didn't deal with what needed dealing with, it would have reared up its ugly head further on down the line, or maybe forever and in many different ways.

I am for the first time in my life getting to know myself, seeing and changing the patterns of my self and my life. Doing more of what works and less of what doesn't. WRAP gets you to the stuff you need to deal with and the changes you need to make in order to move forward.

Finding a meaning and a reason to recover/change is integral to the recovery process. Working as a group in our WRAP classes, we share our strategies for small but powerful changes, and for the first time in my life I have a vision for the life I want to lead.

My family has also directly and indirectly benefited from the program. I teach my family and friends about WRAP; they too are awakening to recovery and taking back control over their own lives.

We recently used WRAP to help our son who was being bullied at school to understand why it was happening and to strategize ways of addressing and dealing with the situation and its outcomes. ॐ

9

I was diagnosed with major depression, anorexia nervosa, and severe anxiety disorder at approximately sixteen years old. My eating disorder controlled my life. I withdrew from others to starve and destroy myself because of the self-hatred I possessed.

In my case, I had to learn to become more self-reliant and not let the scale control my mood and let my size rule my life. I had to face my feelings. Anorexia has allowed triggers to become more prevalent. WRAP has enabled me to face triggers by using coping skills to deal with my stress, figure out my warning signs, which are getting on the scale too often, isolating, restricting my food intake and exercising excessively. Along with depression, my illness can entail irritability, anger, and suicidal tendencies—thus putting into effect the crisis plan and recovery action plan. From the information in WRAP I have learned one final and vital protocol— that social contact and support are essential for me.

With WRAP I have discovered hope among my despair. I am thinking of furthering my education and helping others in emotional distress. My bachelor's degree and work were geared in the social sciences, but due to depression I could not continue pursuing that aspect in my life. I am very analytical and love to do research. I am fearful of people and this is one outlet that will not interfere with my intellectual ability.

10
It is Never Too Late to Do a Wellness Recovery Action Plan

When a person is feeling well and being productive, often we forget (thank God!) the difficulties that we have had in the past and all the suffering that went with those hard times. Unfortunately, we often do not want to think about getting sick again, so we fill our days with people, events and things. The needed preparations for those hard times are often sidetracked and overlooked.

I did well on my medication (Lithium and Navane) for seventeen years. During that time I organized a two-day training in WRAP from Mary Ellen. We got a hands-on training that we busily promoted. However, what happened to my own WRAP? I did not want to face the fact that I was not doing as well as I thought with relationships with family, and friends, and my social life. I simply did not want to face the reality that I did not have anyone in my life that could help me with my disorder during a time of crises. To my detriment, I did not complete a WRAP for myself.

I was in denial and the hurt below the denial was too much for me to handle. I avoided thinking about future episodes by not concretely looking at myself and my life. As you can guess, I ran headfirst into five years of pain, heartache, and despair.

I had decided to try the new wonder drugs on the market which were promoted so smartly by their manufacturers. My doctor kept me on the new drugs and simply added to the cocktail more and more new drugs when they failed to control the voices, the delusions and tactile hallucinations. In fact, the more new drugs my doctor gave to me, the more symptoms of schizoaffective disorder appeared. I had never heard voices even in my earlier hospitalizations.

So determined to be a "good patient," I simply did not want to accept the responsibility of my own pain nor the way my life was turning out. My "excellent compliance" masked the irresponsibility I had in making positive mental health decisions that I, of all people, should have known better. As a consumer and working as a trainer in recovery for mental illness, I did not take my own advice. I simply did not object to adding new drugs. Paradoxically, as I sank deeper and deeper into both physical and psychological pain, the less I was asserting myself. My psychiatrist was growing inpatient and careless as I failed to "respond" to all the medications she was giving me.

I was hospitalized three times in five years. The first two times they kept me on the new drugs. However, the third hospitalization was different. I had gone to Ireland equipped with the latest array of new drugs—five different anti-psychotics plus lithium and an anti-depressant. I was overmedicated, and that was an understatement. Without a WRAP to direct my recovery, I was in big trouble, to say the least.

I knew I was over medicated, so as the pain increased beyond my tolerance, I did the only thing I could think of. I went off all my medication "cold turkey" in a country resort among the hills of Ireland. I was so sick. I paced. I did not sleep. I got the "shakes." I threw-up. I stayed behind in the hotel room as the others on the tour went to see the sights. How would I get home? How would I manage security and customs at the airport? How would I survive the eight hour flight? My thoughts raced. The delusions and audio hallucinations gradually slowed, but the mania was taking over. All I wanted was to get home and get admitted into the mental health hospital that I was familiar with. I was terrified that I would be left behind in a psychiatric hospital in Ireland where I did not know the unspoken rules and customs of being an inpatient. I was scared, so very scared. I did not allow myself to think about dying alone in a foreign country.

They say that the most important part of recovery from mental health disorders is our connectedness with other people and our relationships. I survived my ordeal in Ireland only because I had one friend traveling with me. She turned out to be the best friend in the world. (We are still very close today.) Several times a day she checked in on me. She brought me food. She took me on walks. We walked arm in arm through the streets of Limerick looking for a pharmacy to buy over the counter sleeping medicine. She literally had to hold me up to keep me from falling. I was so sick and all I wanted to do was to get home to America. I did not want to think about how I had ruined my vacation to Ireland. I just wanted to get home. Home to the good 'ole' U.S.A.

Somehow I managed security, customs in Shannon, Ireland, and the O'Hare Airport in Chicago with my friend and her husband. I was finally home. I fell into a deep sleep, once home in my own bed. However, I woke up in a panic. I have to get to the hospital. Now! Immediately! I knew I could not drive. I called 911. I had no plan for how to get to the hospital. I was not thinking. The paramedics first took me to the emergency room and there I told them in a loud voice, stereotyping myself, "I am a mental patient and I need to get to the mental hospital." Surprised, they looked at me and said "Oh, you will go voluntarily?" I nodded my head. I have to admit I was not totally out-of-it. I remember one doctor referring to the mental health hospital by saying: "In my country, we call it 'a place of reconditioning.'" I thought to myself, "that's interesting".

This hospitalization was actually the beginning of my recovery. I had a young female doctor who asked how I had stayed out of the hospital for such a long time (17 years). She replied by saying, "I am going to put you on the same medication." In a few days the medication started to take affect, and I began to slowly regain my balance.

I returned to work in three months. Previously, I had been off work for two years (when I was on the new drugs) after my second hospitalization in those five years. I was back on the "old" drugs, Lithium and Navane. I was busy re-building my career.

So was it too late to do a WRAP? No. I had learned that health, including mental health, has no guarantees, even for someone who works in the mental health field. I sat down and re-read the red WRAP book Mary Ellen had given me. I knew who I could count on in the future — I wrote down simply "me." I had to face the cold reality that I was the only person who would benefit from a WRAP. And that I could help myself. I had to. There was no one in my life that could FIX me but me.

I had not taken my own advice that I had preached so actively. I paid a high price for that neglect—five years of my life. Oh, what a high price to pay, but I knew the past was the past. However, the present and the future were my responsibility and I needed to make those years good years. Very good years.

I completed my WRAP. When psychiatric Advance Directives became law in my state (a project I worked on for 6 years), I used my WRAP to organize and write my Advance Directive. I review my WRAP periodically to keep in mind what good mental health entails. If I need to adjust it as I regain wellness, strength, and empowerment I do so.

No, it is never too late to create and implement a WRAP. I feel much more confident that I know myself better and know more about planning for the hard times as well as learning about wellness and recovery. I feel more secure knowing that I have a plan that works in both the good times and the painful times.

I have yet to start planning overseas trips, but on my next trip to a foreign country I can guarantee that my WRAP is coming with me. Hopefully, my next trip will be a domestic one—to the Copeland Center in Vermont to learn how to become a WRAP facilitator so I can directly help others create their WRAP and Advance Directive. It is never too late to learn. ❧

11

For almost 20 years I dealt with depression, anxiety, and alcoholism. During these years, I was not aware of the depression or anxiety. I knew something was wrong and alcohol was the "medication" I used to ease the pain. After I sobered up, I not only became majorly depressed, and I also had no skills to let anyone *really* know what was going on. The coping skills I had used in my life had been few: alcohol and turning inward (not letting emotions out).

In October of 2005, I was hospitalized. After I was released from the hospital, my new therapist suggested I go to a day program. I started going and a whole new world opened up to me. Here was a place I could go and attend groups about coping skills, relapse prevention, stress management and so much more!

After attending for several weeks, I was asked if I would attend a Mental Health Recovery Seminar. The seminar focused on using WRAP for recovery. I was fascinated with Mary Ellen Copeland's story. Her story gave me hope for my own future. I also was fascinated with the WRAP workbook I received at the seminar. I now had a place to write down my triggers (first I had to identify my triggers,) what I can do to offset the triggers (coping skills) and how to recover. I look over my WRAP book every day. I use the Wellness Toolbox (certain things I can do help me stay well and help relieve my symptoms) all the time as a reminder of what I need to do for myself.

A load has been lifted off my shoulders since I completed my Crisis Plan and Post Crisis Plan. People I choose will help me in specific areas and ways. I had to ask these people if they would help and in what way could they help me in a crisis situation. WRAP has changed my life. I now know what my triggers are. I now have coping skills to use to offset my triggers and symptoms. I now know I can recover. I can recover because of my use of WRAP in my everyday life and because of the help of all the wonderful and understanding people I work with everyday. I will recover because I now have the tools and the talent to recover. ୬

12

The first time I heard about WRAP, I was sitting in my therapist's office. I was full of rage, recently diagnosed, hopeless, fed up and a whole bunch of other overwhelming things I could not identify at the time. I agreed to attend a WRAP group with the idea that maybe someone could fix me. I knew what I had been doing wasn't working so I was willing to let someone else try. Little did I know what was in store for me!

I attended my first WRAP group expecting things to be very different than they were. One of the facilitators was physically very similar to my mother and I had a hard time not running out of the room when I saw her. Later I would identify this as a trigger through the use of WRAP. I did not run out of the room that day. I sat still and listened, waiting patiently for someone to try to fix me. I had been in and out of the Mental Health system since the age of 15 when my parents divorced and I experienced my first suicidal ideation. So I was pretty sure I knew what to expect from this group, but I was wrong. Instead of the facilitators trying to fix me, they enabled me to see inside myself the answers I really desperately sought.

Through very simple steps I began to see myself and the world around me differently. I began to see that trusting someone would not always lead to heartache. I learned about Peer Support Specialists and WRAP Facilitators. The people sharing things that were helping were just like me. Very early into WRAP, I set a goal to take all the classes I needed to share these skills with others—A goal I was pretty sure I couldn't reach, but I really wanted what my facilitators seemed to have.

I began to use WRAP, make friends, and move out of constant crisis. I began to identify things in my life that were good and things I might need to work on. I had a plan when I went into crisis and was able to transition back into my routine much easier having a WRAP. I completed WRAP classes twice before I decided to move two hours from where I was living. And not before I had signed up to take the Peer Support class being offered at the center I had been attending. I drove the distance back towards my old home to take this class and the WRAP Facilitator class as well.

Things have not been easy for me on many occasions since that first day in WRAP, but now I have the tools to better cope with what comes my way. WRAP gave me a drive for wellness I had never before known or seen. I still struggle with the shyness that came from the childhood abuse my mother was quick to dole out, with anger, fear, and trouble self-advocating and many other things. Life has not quit coming at me, I have changed the way I allow it to affect me.

I went to work in the mental health profession two months ago and have started my first WRAP group with the prospect of several more to come. WRAP drives me, and I am now able to see in others' eyes what my facilitators must have seen in mine, the return of hope. ❧

13

When I first went to a WRAP class I was there because I was extremely angry at the whole world and everybody in it. I was Mr. Negative! But as the class continued I started to listen to the class facilitators. Slowly but surely, more slowly than surely, I began to hear what these extraordinary people had to say.

I was set back by their own personal stories. They were human and not actors. It dawned on me that if they could talk about their past problems and recover, why couldn't I? As the class proceeded, the more I went, the more I became interested in what they had to say. Slowly my eyes were opened to the horror of what my problem was.

I had found fault with everyone but me! I slowly emerged into a new human being that I hadn't seen in a long, long time. My outlook and my disposition changed and because of the class and the facilitators and their stories, I am in recovery. I am now taking the Peer Support Class and hope to be part of this fantastic and wonderful movement called, WRAP & Peer Support Specialist.

Thank you for the wonderful gift you have given us, who gave up hope in ourselves, and because of what you have done and are doing, give us the courage to go on with our NEW lives. ❧

14

My WRAP story began in 1992 in a town I had escaped to so that no one would know I had mental illness, a place where I could avoid being treated as a diagnosis, first, and the person I was second. The only mental illness reality I had known, was an uncle who "was," but I didn't know "what." I knew he had long stays in our state hospital and I remembered the occasional trips there, waiting in the car as my mother went through the locked doors and into a building that didn't welcome her. My uncle never appeared outside of it. Throughout my childhood, he would take off when he could and follow the circus, until my grandmother needed to bring him home again, back to the hospital and more days behind locked doors. In those days circuses had great acts, but also had the freaks of society on display. I don't know if he followed them to recapture a childhood that didn't go haywire as an adult or if he felt as an adult, he fit in with the misfits that were there. When I met Mary Ellen, my daughter was living with my ex-husband for no reason other than my having a diagnosis. My career died the day the company psychiatrist labeled me. My family, while supportive, treated me with kid gloves, and the stigma that came from everywhere came from me the most. I went to a new town with my secret and a deck of index cards that I used to monitor my symptoms. I kept the index cards in my purse, to be used any time I felt being "different" creeping up on me. I checked in every morning and night, going through each one and making sure any symptoms I felt, I dealt with the best way I could.

I moved into a house within walking distance to the hospital, just in case, and began a job as a clerk in the local department store, a job I enjoyed in a town that I could relax in, but a life that wasn't really me. I left who I was behind, back in my hometown as I sought something closer to the me that I remembered and longed for.

At the department store I met many friends and felt respected for the person I let them see. Of course, my self respect and living an authentic life wasn't really there, but I have always been one to "fake it, till you make it" with the best of them.

One day, I was walking around town and looked into a bookstore. Sitting on a couch was a woman who seemed to be the center of attention, laughing and talking with what appeared to be the whole town, or at least many people that I had seen here and there and were fast becoming what I thought of as the fabric of this community.

I hesitated to walk in and become a part of this celebration and longingly wanted to feel what I could only imagine this woman was feeling, something I remembered feeling so long ago. I slipped my hand into my purse and held my index cards for a moment. Touching them gave me the strength to know that I was doing well and allowed me to walk into the door and into what appeared to be a group of normal people celebrating life, a life that appealed to me.

I wandered around the perimeter of the group and gathered my confidence to approach them closer and see what the fuss over this woman was all about.

I can't adequately express in words, what happened to me at the moment that I realized this town was celebrating her and a book she had written titled *Living Without Depression and Manic Depression*. I can tell you what happened inside of me at that moment; I felt light, a burden lifted and the flow of hope throughout my body—hope that can't be defined by words, just experienced. I knew at that moment, I would go home again and with me I would be taking a book and the scene of a woman, with a diagnosis like mine being a central part of her community. The knowledge that she could do it meant I could again. For the first time since I experienced psychosis, I felt I belonged. Not to any one place, but to me, the person that I lost years ago when I became a diagnosis first and a person second. I realized that wasn't true just by witnessing this scene. When Mary Ellen invited me to sit on that couch next to her, I knew that I would never again let anyone put my diagnosis before *me*, because I saw there was at least one place and one person that it didn't happen to.

Mary Ellen became a friend. Not a friend that I would call or correspond with on a regular basis, but a friend that shared her hope with me, given to her by her amazing strength and her community and given to me to surround myself with and return to my community to share.

I knew this was a gift and not a gift meant just for me, but one meant for others too. "Pay it Forward" might describe it now, but back then it was simple for me that hope is for each of us, and like Mary Ellen, I would share it with those around me.

Once home, I convinced our local hospital to hire Mary Ellen to come and speak. When they first reacted with, "We won't be able to fill an auditorium to discuss depression," I replied, "You can if you want, this woman is worth it and I will help." Mary Ellen agreed to come to our clubhouse for free to share with those that wouldn't be able to get scholarships to attend the day the hospital organized for her.

I watched as people caught Mary Ellen's vision of hope, personal responsibility, education, self-advocacy, and support. Oprah's "aha moment" doesn't begin to describe the gift of life being renewed for those around me, simply by Mary Ellen sharing the hope she found within herself and from her mother.

Mary Ellen continued to write more books and I turned to advocacy training and advocating against stigma, replacing words that took away my hope with words that gave it back to me. I went on to spend a few years working at a university research center and coordinating our state's involvement in a national multi-site study. My goal was promoting Mary Ellen's work whenever I could.

I went on to convince a woman from our local mental health agency and a researcher to help me to bring WRAP to my hometown. Consulting with Mary Ellen, the researcher defined each part of WRAP as "evidence based" and we were awarded a Community Action Grant in 2000 to build consensus within my community to create what I knew would be a center of education and hope.

I relapsed, but managed to continue. I could only do this based on my WRAP, my commitment and the commitment of those also inspired by Mary Ellen. We went on to obtain state funding and hire an Executive Director in 2001. I left my dream in her hands. I went on to concentrate on my recovery and taking care of my parents during the end of their lives.

As I became well again and was deciding my place once more, I was living again in a community that wasn't mine, missing myself. My WRAP worked to an extent, but not completely. Medication side effects were preventing my recovery skills from working and were preventing me from knowing why. Once off the medication, I knew why recovery wasn't connecting to me again, and it was simply that I was once again disconnected from hope and the principles of WRAP.

One day, I was sitting on a smoking porch listening to a woman I had just met and her excitement for herself and her family. She told me how her brother was in a state hospital and until now was seemingly lost to them forever. Nothing worked, nothing touched him and he was a shell of the brother she grew up with and loved. Today though, she told me that he connected—connected with something amazing, brought life within him and a newfound dedication to recovery. I asked her what happened. With tears in her eyes, she looked at me and said "My brother went to a WRAP class." It was put on by the agency I had started. She excitedly told me of the changes in him and the relief she felt that she would have her brother back and asked me if I knew about WRAP. I told her I did, and thanked her for telling me about her brother. I knew at that moment it was time for me to go back home and back to a community that inspires me. It was time to reconnect and time for me to remember the very important principles of hope and support, done the WRAP way. ক্ষ

15
Story of Recovery

I grew up in a time and place where we knew nothing about mental illness. While the down side of this was that my illness went untreated, the upside was that I didn't receive any labels or treatment that would have caused me to think of myself as "sick." Even though I got more spankings than other kids did and received negative messages from teachers and various other adults, I didn't think of myself as damaged. My parents didn't know how to help me, or what to do with me, but they did love me, and this, along with the strong spiritual competencies I developed early on, is probably what got me through. In retrospect, I was struggling with serious levels of depression and anxiety through most of my teens and early adulthood.

I attended a small college where I knew the instructors and was able to fit in. I've never been a brilliant student, but my determination and occasional high levels of energy allowed me to persevere the endurance test of working odd jobs and going to school at the same time. Once I graduated I found a job with a welfare department. This gave me opportunities to serve others and I found that this helped me a lot. In fact, just working gave me more self-confidence and a sense of meaning and purpose in my life that helped counteract the serious symptoms I was dealing with.

I had an opportunity to go back to school part-time through my job, so I began to earn credits toward a master's degree in social work. Again, my occasional high energy level and the perseverance that I had learned from dealing with symptoms allowed me to complete the two-year program (in three years) and earn an MSW degree.

Thanks to my health insurance, I had been able to see a series of psychotherapists during part of this time, which had helped me understand what I was dealing with. Still, I saw myself as a normal person who was facing challenges that I needed help with. I will never forget the day that I was sitting in a therapist's office, and realized that I had something wrong with me. That I was different, that I was sick. This came as a huge blow to me. Once I bought in to having an illness, it shook me to the core. This moment is different for all of us. Some of us are relieved to find that what we are dealing with has a name, and we aren't just being lazy or irresponsible, but for me, this moment was devastating. My confidence slipped and my symptoms got worse. It was during this time that my boss noticed how hard I had to struggle—operating over the top of symptoms—in order to do my work. He thought that I might benefit from medication and suggested I see a psychiatrist.

Taking medication was hard at first. There weren't many options in those days. I kept trying to work while taking various medications and had some very embarrassing moments of falling asleep in meetings, and not being able to stand up without getting too dizzy. Finally through trial and error, I found a medication that was helpful that began to relieve the symptoms.

It took about six months before I could see the light of day, and once I did I was so grateful for the medication. It allowed me to direct the energy I was investing in managing symptoms into more creative areas that were rewarding and validating. I still struggled with symptoms, self-esteem, and with concerns that someone would find out how damaged I was. I lived with a constant fear that someone inside me would go berserk and without any warning would make me really sick and insane. I had no idea that I could recover—that wasn't even on my "to-do" list. Surviving was my goal. Pat Deegan tells us that "the goal is not to be normal, but to be more of who we really are," and she is so right. But at that point in my life I was hoping to act normal enough to continue hiding. I told no one about my illness, not even my family. I was ashamed, and afraid if people found out I would never be given a chance to do anything.

I was able to function at a credible level with the medication and continually got promoted into management positions. Haunted by that someone inside me, and always being afraid of not being good enough, or well enough, or smart enough, propelled me into another masters program and I earned a second Master's degree in Public Administration.

My first inkling of recovery came during this period when I would sit across the table from people I was working with, realizing that we were struggling with the same symptoms, and taking the same medications. Our similarities gave me tremendous empathy for what people were going through and at the same time I knew they were more than their symptoms, as was I—fragile though we were. Since we shared so much common ground, I wasn't tempted to see myself as "better than" them. If I could be on this side of the table, so could they. I wondered how I had been able to be on the "well" side of the table and the best I could come up with was not that I had stumbled into ways of recovering, but that I had been able to fool everyone and that it was just a matter of time before they found out and fired me.

A few years later I went back to school (evening and weekends of course) and earned a Ph.D. in Psychology, yet the more I learned, the less I knew the answer to my question about the sides of the table. I only had more questions. I continued to take lots of medication, and managed to earn a couple additional diagnoses. The work I was doing was making less sense to me and some of it felt like a charade where both the "treaters" and the "treatees" had unconsciously agreed to play their parts with neither getting much satisfaction from the script. Something wasn't right about it. I didn't know how to articulate it but I knew there was something about the way we were delivering services that lacked integrity.

Then it happened. I started reading about recovery. One night I was sitting at my computer and I found Mary Ellen's web site and read the story of Kate and was very moved. I told my husband, "We have to meet this woman," and within a few weeks we were at one of her trainings. Mary Ellen's generosity and her caring spirit gave me hope and confidence not only that I could recover, but that I could figure out how to help others recover too. The WRAP that she and her group developed has been a great help to me in my recovery.

When I first completed my WRAP, I realized that there was something I could do to manage that someone inside me. I had some say over my symptoms, and WRAP was the key to managing them and staying well. The more I used WRAP, the more confidence I gained in my ability to be well. I no longer read my WRAP on a regular basis because it has become a part of me. I am able to see the red flags ahead and choose a better course for myself.

Now, eight years after completing my first WRAP, I look back and see the key role it played in my recovery and I am very grateful.

16

My recovery story begins during one of my many psychiatric hospitalizations. I was told it was time for group and the staff was going to show a video. After many hospitalizations I wasn't very hopeful that I would learn anything through attending another group. Boy, was I wrong!

That day they showed your video, the one where you tell Kate's story. That story was the first message of hope in a three-year struggle with mental illness. After seeing that particular video I thought if Kate could recover after eight years, maybe I could recover after three. Thus my introduction to WRAP and the concept and hope that I too could recover.

Following my local hospitalization, I spent over three months at a large out of state facility. During that hospitalization I worked with a psychologist that was familiar with WRAP and I wrote my first WRAP plan.

Following that hospitalization I returned home. However, I called the Copeland Center before I even left the hospital to see where there was a trained facilitator in my area. Lo and behold, one of the two trained facilitators in the entire state was in the community that I was going to.

Shortly after I reached home, the trained facilitator offered WRAP at the local community hospital. I attended those sessions and continued to learn about the concept of recovery and wellness tools that I could use as I began to rebuild my life. At one of our sessions I must have indicated that I wasn't doing real well. My facilitator asked me if I wanted to stay after and talk with her. I did. During that conversation, I admitted that my birthday was coming up over the weekend and I had no intention of surviving. My facilitator was awesome. She did not haul me off for yet another hospitalization; instead she helped me develop a plan to stay safe. Over the course of that weekend I touched base with her several times. A short time later, I read a quote attributed to Mary Ellen that said at one point you made a conscious decision that suicide was no longer an option. I took that to heart and arrived at the same conclusion. I cannot stress enough how important it is for persons suffering from serious suicidal ideation to eventually make a conscious decision that suicide is no longer an option. Prior to that point I didn't care if I committed suicide fast with an overdose of medication or slowly by neglecting my diabetes and high blood pressure.

When I started to use my WRAP plan, I had one item on my daily maintenance list—to get out of bed. Not shower, brush my teeth, eat breakfast or even get dressed. It was simply one thing, to get out of bed.

At this point my daily maintenance plan allows me to work full time, dress and groom myself properly, manage my diabetes and today I have joy in my life. This is the healthiest I have ever been physically, mentally, emotionally or spiritually.

As I said at the beginning, following participation in the WRAP course and refining my WRAP plan, I was able to become a Certified WRAP Facilitator. Our state now has 144 trained WRAP facilitators. I believe with my whole heart that I am alive today because of WRAP. As I teach WRAP groups, I continue to learn new recovery tools and incorporate them into my life. My life today is better than I ever dreamed it could be. I live independently, I have a car, I work full time as a Recovery Support Specialist and I have someone special in my life that cares about me and my well-being. 🐦

17

My name is _____ and I live and facilitate WRAP in my state. I wish that I had known about WRAP, particularly the Post Crisis Plan, when I was hospitalized at the state hospital five years ago. I came out of the hospital with symptoms still strong, as they had me on the wrong medication. I was in the hospital for a month, went home for a month and returned to the hospital a month later for two weeks. I left against doctor's orders but was there on a volunteer basis.

If I had known about the Post Crisis Plan, I would have lined up friends to take me grocery shopping. I was eating nothing but pinto beans and rice and got down from 140 lbs. to 108 lbs —skin and bones. I also could have had friends to take me to the outpatient daily, as they did not trust me to take my own medications at home on my own. I had many friends who brought in Twelve Step meetings to the hospital for me and took me to meetings when I returned home. I did not know about setting these things up before I went into the hospital so therefore I did not access these friends.

Also, I was so paranoid because of the obscene voices which continued all the time when I was awake. I covered the windows with plastic bags so no one could see in and did not answer the door or the phone for several months. The only time I didn't hear the voices is when I was asleep, so I slept almost all the time. Then I would have horrific dreams about things I would never even think of doing.

A friend gave me a coin about 6 months after I got out of the hospital. On one side it said, "you may be hopeless," on the other, "but you are not helpless." I thought about this for awhile and after a month went to a staffing with my psychiatrist, case manager, nurse, etc. and told them I was still hearing voices and asked what was the shrink going to do about it. He said, and I quote, "Well, we'll increase your medications to 100 mg." I told him, "You can do anything you damn well please, but I am not taking any medication except what has been proven to work in the past." He said he had to talk with my treatment guardian, and I asked him if she was a psychiatrist and he said she wasn't. "So why are you consulting her?" I asked. At any rate, after a week, he changed my meds to the one I knew would work, and *get this*, within a week the voices were gone. So I went through hell for ten months before I learned to advocate for myself.

I share this part of my recovery to students of WRAP so that they can advocate for themselves in their treatment plan and making decisions about medications. ॐ

18
WRAP: An Integral Part of My Recovery

I believe, as a consumer of mental health services, there is a lot to deal with once we, in our community, are diagnosed with a disorder, disease, or disability. When I reflect on these words, they resonate to me an absence of order in my life, lack of ease in living and less ability to accomplish my goals.

Being aware of having several mental health diagnoses, has, in one sense, explained, perhaps justified, my past unsettling behavior. Accepting these diagnoses, however, has been a continual ode to perseverance, and above all, faith; faith that I can live a healthy, productive, meaningful life with order, ease and ability.

In 2002, I started volunteering with a Peer Bridger Program. This program was a wonderful transition for me. I had just graduated from a psychosocial rehabilitation program and needed continual structure and purpose in my life. The Peer Bridger Program Coordinator at that time introduced me to the WRAP Plan. He stressed the importance of having this plan and the benefits of incorporating it into my life, as WRAP promotes wellness and recovery—something a peer providing support, resources and especially, hope, to other peers (consumers of mental health services) must have, in order to be effective in helping others.

Since Mary Ellen Copeland is a consumer herself, she truly understands the issues I go through. She takes medication, she sees a doctor... she's been here. For these reasons, the WRAP has been that much more effective in my recovery, as I am following the example of someone truly dedicated to their recovery. With WRAP, there is no shame in experiencing my symptoms or even being in crisis; there is, however, the element of personal responsibility, a key concept of recovery. I knew I must ask myself the question, "Am I perpetuating my wellness or my illness?"

Since my first WRAP Plan was established in 2002, I have continued to refer to it and work it (and many times, revise it!). I now have the privilege of facilitating two WRAP classes. In conclusion, WRAP is an integral part of maintaining my mental health. Additionally, I credit the support of my Higher Power, my family, all the health care professionals involved in my recovery, my friends and peers. They have inspired me, as I hope to inspire others, to celebrate wellness and recovery. ⁊

19

I had read about WRAP many years ago when I read a book about fibromyalgia co-authored by Mary Ellen Copeland. It seemed like a good idea. I took parts and applied them to my life, but didn't formally adopt the program.

In June of 2003, I became a widow. I was faced for the first time with the situation of not being supported. After the initial shock, I began thinking about working part-time. I had many ups and downs over the next 2 years, dealing with the grief, raising my children and working with my mental and physical illnesses. I attended a psychosocial rehabilitation program near my home off and on. I also volunteered at different recovery groups on several committees, as a way to learn about recovery and supplement my income.

In June of 2004, I ended up in the hospital with severe depression. I was reintroduced to the WRAP when a medication group viewed the WRAP tape. It started to come back to me. I worked with one of the staff to develop a WRAP notebook. I felt empowered and started to climb out of my depression.

In September of 2005, I had the opportunity to participate in a two-day workshop. I was also attending a 16-week long training to become a Peer Specialist and attending the local community college part-time. It was a full plate. I was stretching my wings as far as I could.

In October, 2005, I was picked to attend a week long training to become a facilitator. I took a week off school. The pace of all this was intense but I thought that with my WRAP plan I could do it. Midweek

I started to get a respiratory illness. Having a WRAP wasn't enough. Several weeks later I ended up hospitalized for a week. I wrote another WRAP while in the hospital, using the tools to figure out what went wrong and to plan another strategy. Writing the WRAP allowed me to feel as if I was in charge of my health for the first time. I shared my WRAP plan with anyone who came into my room and would listen! Telling it over and over helped cement it in my mind.

After six weeks at home, I returned to school and my other training. I was determined to try and get out of the dry dock. I thought keeping my WRAP plan in my head was enough. In December of 2005, I ended up hospitalized again for depression. I brought my WRAP plan and again looked back to see where I went wrong. I made another plan. Again, I talked to everyone I could about it. I showed it to all my doctors. I was out in a week this time.

In 2006 I started back to school. I am also part of my agency's WRAP team. We planned to do an eight-week session for one of our residential sites. In January, I met with my new psychiatrist and introduced him to WRAP and talked about how this was going to help keep me well. I was started on some new medication.

In February I started to get sick again. I was anxious beyond belief. I was having a lot of physical symptoms as well. A lot of snafus were happening in terms of my switching over to community mental health for therapy and scripts. I kept to my WRAP plan to help me feel in control. I couldn't understand why I was getting sick again. I finally got to see the doctor and he told me I was having a reaction to the drug. Because I had a WRAP plan, I was able to stay out of the hospital! I rewrote my WRAP plan again, tweaking it.

After a couple of months, I began thinking about working again. I began making plans with my coach about how to go about it. I wrote a WRAP plan for this goal. My team is planning another WRAP session. I plan to be there this time.

Having a WRAP plan is about writing and following it, but it is also about showing your treatment team that you are serious about being an active part, a proactive part. Having a WRAP helped me to talk to those on my treatment team and to feel empowered. It gave me confidence. It is like having a diploma from the prestigious school of hard knocks. Professionals respect it. They respect me. I respect me. 👒

20

I am a forty-one-year old woman who has manic depression and borderline personality disorders. All through my life I have had snapshots when one or both disorders appear. I never understood any of the signs and symptoms. I just thought that was just how it is. But then the worst thing in the world happened, a mother's nightmare. My three-month baby girl was abused in day care. My symptoms started to spin out of control from mania to depression. I was unable to perform even the smallest of some tasks, let alone perform my duty in the military.

In October 1999 my doctor diagnosed me with manic depressive disorder (bi-polar). But that was just the start of my new-found life. In April of 2000, the military, which I have given 14 years of faithful service to, gave me a medical discharge with honors. Just when I was feeling safe with my doctors, my husband was transferred. Now I had to find new doctors as well as acclimate to base housing. Yet my life was in a rapid cycle of mania and depression along with paranoia.

In March of 2002 I committed a crime in my neighborhood. In November I was found not guilty due to mental defect or illness. I was placed in a forensic hospital for almost three years. There I was also diagnosed with borderline personality disorder.

To help me with these disorders I was introduced to the Wellness Recovery Action Plan (WRAP). I spent the next year and a half researching and creating my own personal WRAP book. My research for my WRAP is far from being completed. Each situation, place, and person helps me make my WRAP stronger. I also know my WRAP will change throughout my lifetime.

I am now in a less secure hospital, but I still wanted to use my WRAP as soon as possible. After my morning routine, I read my WRAP for about 20 to 30 minutes. This way I have a positive start on my day. I have days where I am working my WRAP and have a great day. Then I have days where I cannot get through the blocks that are in front of me. This is when the WRAP book puts on the Superman cape. The first thing is to find out the trigger/early warning signs. Then find the right tool(s) to help. If it was a new trigger/early warning sign, I find the tools(s) that are as close as possible or make a new one. The more I practice, the better my day-to-day activity has become. My biggest struggle is my uncertain future. My family is moving, this time without me. Every time my sadness brings me back to why I am here, I pull out my WRAP Book. I look for the home and comfort in the different exercises my WRAP book offers. Life for me now is like walking a tight wire, but now I have my WRAP book as my safety net. The WRAP is also like my medication. I still keep using it, even if I feel better, to be able to anticipate and avoid severe moods in both disorders. My WRAP book has all the answers for me and my family.

There are days when I cannot catch the warning sign or even the trigger. I know it is impossible to rely on my support group 100%. When some crises happen, I still have the feeling to hide and put on a tough guy look. Slowly, as I study more on myself, and also using the guidelines of the WRAP book and other self-helpful books, I am becoming more aware of "When Things Start to Break Down," "Triggers," and "Early Warning Signs." My WRAP Book is very useful when the pressure of the hospital ward is so overwhelming I cannot breathe, let along think. Sometimes I just want to throw my hands up and say, "I give up and I don't want to care." Even with the WRAP I still feel unsure, but not as much as I did in 2000. So, little by little, things are getting easier. Having a plan helps, just like any other program. It only works if you want it to.

I just wish I knew about the WRAP after I was diagnosed. Then maybe I wouldn't have the status of being dangerously mental ill. I still have shame about what happened. I am facing the loss of my children. But for now my WRAP Book and I are on a day-to-day mission. This has shown me how to cope with anything that comes my way and more.

Thank you so much for listening to my story. I just hope I can reach one person, so they know how important it is to take your medication, listen to your doctors, and become involved in a recovery program. Life as a 330.20 (a legal term for criminally insane) is not fun. Please, please get help some way if you think something is wrong. ❧

21
My Experience

When things are breaking down—I start my story at the end of my WRAP plan. Why do I start my story at the end? Well, simply put, it's because that's where I am at the moment. *No joke!*

Hello everyone. Who am I, you ask? I'm a person who was introduced to WRAP a year ago. Why was I introduced to WRAP? I was introduced to WRAP along with other coping groups via an intensive outpatient day treatment program sponsored by a hospital. But why? The why is the interesting part. I hope so anyway.

I'm a 38 year-old woman who was diagnosed with bipolar disorder in my mid-thirties. I also suffered a traumatic brain injury (TBI) in 1996 as a result of an automobile accident.

The question remains: Why am I starting the story at the end? I'm starting at the part of WRAP "When things are breaking down" because things are breaking down for me at the present. I now find myself in the middle of a manic episode that is only escalating in nature. What happened? How did this happen? Very good questions.

I was stable and have been for four months. Yes, four months! You see, I was discharged from an in-patient mental health unit on February 21, 2006. I was sent home with my WRAP crisis plan to insure my safety. As a matter of fact, I was moving into a community residence at the time and before I was allowed to move in, the director of the residence made sure I had my crisis plan completed, along with other parts of WRAP. So work hard I did! I worked at the WRAP crisis plan while I was still an in-patient at the hospital, before moving into my new home. That's how valuable WRAP was to everyone involved with my treatment.

You say, "So what happened so that I've become unstable?" Well, I was put on a medication that caused me to gain 40 pounds very rapidly. And I argued with my psychiatrist, as I think any woman would, to "get me off this med." She only conceded after my primary care physician got involved and showed concern about my rapid weight gain in so little time (given the history of diabetes in my family). The only problem now is that it was the only medication that seemed to stabilize me after months of trying while I was in-patient in the hospital. Now I'm feeling the aftermath of being taken off of it. Was I a fool? Only you could tell me.

I open my WRAP folder and look back at things such as my "Daily Maintenance List" and know I'm in trouble because even though the problem I'm having now involves a medication change, there were things I could have been doing on my "Daily Maintenance List" that would have eased these symptoms that I'm now having. I know I would be in a better spot, coping with all that "bipolar" has to "offer" me. I'd be singing, "Hit me with your best shot." *a la* Pat Benatar. No kidding!

And that's what WRAP means to me. It's an opportunity to be able to cope with mental illness. Much like a bodyguard safeguards a person, WRAP safeguards me, including times where it might have to protect me from myself. I know I wasn't doing the things that keep me on the straight and narrow, things such as exercise, eating healthy meals, keeping myself hydrated, and being sure to take all medications as prescribed. I'm taking all my meds this time, but only because I'm on assisted out-patient treatment. It's a court order instructing me to take my medications, besides a few other things to assure I don't become a threat to myself or others; so if I don't take the meds the director of the residence would be forced to do a 960 on me (call the police so that they may bring me into the hospital for a psychiatric evaluation and possible admission). Why am I telling you all of this? It's because I want you to have hope. I'm positive that if WRAP could help me, it could work for you too.

As I'm writing, I can feel the energy of the mania channel through my fingertips and I find myself coping in a positive way. So I am doing something right. I'm working my crisis plan; and this being one of many positive coping skills that I wrote down for myself to use in times like these. Besides the journaling, I'm also resorting to other things such as reaching out to my supports in a time of crisis, whether by phone or in person. I've been on the telephone all morning. I also have the Crisis Unit as a possibility for a "holding environment" where I could spend the night without necessarily being admitted. The goal being they would discharge me to their day treatment program in the morning when I would be able to see the doctor.

By now you may be thinking, who is this crazy woman? Where does she come from? And what hole did she crawl out of? No, my dear readers, please do not jump to such conclusions. I was much like your ordinary "stay at home mom" who spent her days taking her children to the library for story hour, to gymnastics, and who would arrange "play dates" for her little ones to have the much needed association with their friends. I was a suburban housewife in an upper middle-class neighborhood. I've been married for 16 years and have two beautiful children, a boy and girl. You might say I was living the "life of Riley." But was I?

My dear friends, as I now like to think you are, I was living the life of an imposter. It all smelled of roses on the outside, but inside it was full of venomous snakes and poisonous rats. Who was the snake? And who was the rat? I need not reply except to say I am now in the middle of a legal separation and possible divorce, hence the "slew of attorneys."

I've been the victim of domestic violence during my 16 years of marriage. In 1996, I incurred a traumatic brain injury when I was broadsided by an ambulance that was en route to the hospital transporting a patient who was also in a car accident just moments earlier. In 2004 I was diagnosed with a mental illness. And in 2005 I suffered the results of my second drug overdose, the first being in December of 2004. They were all near lethal attempts during which I suffered cardiac arrest among other things.

But who am I? I'm just a woman with a mental illness struggling to get by. A woman facing the prejudices of a society so not ready to accept mental illness. A woman who was put out of her own home by her husband because he was not ready to accept her mental illness (So much for "in sickness and in health"), and yet I'm a woman who is facing her demons and *winning*!

I have a spiritual life. I believe in God but I also believe that God helps us through programs such as WRAP. We must avail ourselves of the help that is out there.

So in retrospect, as I look at "when things are breaking down," I can readily identify symptoms such as feeling needy, racing thoughts, and inability to slow down; I know I need to turn the page and see what I've outlined for myself to do now. Well, it says, "Let go and let God." I'll read my crisis plan once again and trust that everything will be all right. I do thank God for programs such as WRAP. It's a step-by-step outline of the things I must do to keep myself safe. It walks with me through the ups and downs of my life. It's my companion in time of duress (such as now). And it's also my buddy who reminds me of the basics on my Daily Maintenance list when things are okay. It's my compass, you might say, that keeps me on course. I just must learn to always listen to its cues. It just takes practice and this one workout I don't want to miss.

In the end I know I'll be okay. Everything will be okay. And I've come to realize that, "hey, we're all ok just the way we are!"

The following poem is by the woman who wrote this story:
I wake to a new day.
With scattered thoughts I brave ahead.
What are the thoughts that imprison me?
I know what I feel but is it truth?
I clothed myself with uncertainty and race for my lifeline.
Will God answer the prayer?
I pick up the phone –
I call for help –
I talk it out –
Did I find the answer?
Has inspiration stepped inside?
Has courage found its way into my heart?

I go to my bedroom, with each step heavier than the first.

With my heart racing and blood that is pumping out

of control, I wonder:

Where is that WRAP folder Liz gave me?

I know what I'll do, I'll write my story.

With love, I'll funnel this energy inside me;

Though I am scared, I have too much to lose.

Will I end up on the third floor?

Will the hospital welcome me home again?

Only with time it shall reveal itself

First, I must talk with my "little girl".

Console her –

"It's OK to be different," I tell her

"It is?" Her softness melts my heart.

"Yes, as long as we're different,

the Universe will find meaning." ❧

22

I have a WRAP Plan. My diagnosis is schizophrenia. I went to a series of groups. I gave my WRAP plan to my primary therapist. She is going to keep it in my file. My WRAP plan is simple. Of most help to me is the daily maintenance plan. I was able to list what I need to do to be well. I am not experiencing any symptoms right now. I am working. This is my third year there. I am in subsidized HUD housing in an Independent Living program. I have SSI. I am 59 years old. My condition developed when I was 54 years old. I am divorced. I have three children and two grandchildren. I have a one bedroom apartment. I came across a prayer line that I call when I feel concerned about things I cannot do anything about.

23

I learned of the WRAP program from my supervisor when I started working part time in February 2005. When I first heard about the

WRAP program, I was told about how it helps you with your day-to-day recovery. Also how to cope when you're not feeling well, when things are breaking down, like a death in the family, isolation, financial difficulties and others.

I had worked at a number of different places between May 1989 and April 1997, latch key, as teachers aid, also at a beauty shop as a receptionist, until August of 2004. I was unable to keep these positions because of my mental illness. I did not have any support group of friends, family, church members who were knowledgeable enough to help me at that time, that understood my mental illness.

Out of that despair I was shown how to cope with my illness and still work part time. I learned how to communicate better with people, attend conferences on peer support, I attended a rally sponsored by community mental health, an anti-stigma walk, "Walk a Mile in my Shoes," where we made a political statement at our state capital and met the State Senator and shared with him some of our mental health concerns. I also attended the WRAP Conference in Massachusetts.

There I was encouraged to take the WRAP Facilitator training. The training has taught me how to develop action plans for whatever stage I may be in. For example, there was a suicide death in my family. Because of the program, I was able to come to work when I would have rather stayed at home and isolate. I also called my case manager and shared my concerns with him about my family situation, which was another part of my action plan that I put into place. I was told to stay strong for my family and to call the crisis hotline if needed. I'm finding support from my co-workers. We are able to talk about my concerns as well. Instead of being alone, I find myself surrounded by caring, understanding people who are actively involved in my life.

Prior to the WRAP program I wouldn't have reached out to others for their support. Taking the time to map out the action plan has given me greater control over my personal circumstances.

I'm a peer counselor educator in an activity and education program for consumers. My co-worker and I put together a brochure of activities, such as support groups for women and men, art groups, bowling, and Wellness Recovery Action Planning, just to name a few. We also do a mailing every three months to all people in the agency that receive mental health services. Staff, people who received services, and outside agencies may teach a class.

I have been working for a year and five months now. I do water aerobics three times a week, get my hair and nails done, and don't feel guilty about taking care of my self. I have taken speech crafters class. I also facilitate the WRAP class every Tuesday. I would have not been able to hold this job for this long with out the tools of the WRAP program.

24

I am: wonderful person and venturing person

I wonder: where the next situation leads

I hear: my inner voice and my soundings all around me

I see: see my life play out in amazing ways

I want: so much to get really life

I am: not wandering I am there or falling in foot steps

I pretend: to try on everybody's shoes

I feel: happiness and pain and it is wonderful

I touch: touch a flower and feel its softness

I worry: very little but a little stress

I cry: when I cannot find happiness within people and myself

I am: always smiling and hoping the best for friends and family

I understand: at times how limited things are

I say: I will find a way and head straight for it

I dream: big because anything is possible

I try: every day for quietness and peace within me

I hope: the best for most anything

I am: happy because I can write these things down and dream big

25

I have lived in rural Kansas all of my life and I grew up on a farm. I have had my bipolar 1 mental illness 40 years of my life. I am now 57 years old. I have lived a lot of my adult life in places where I have been hospitalized and now live in an area that I call home. I have been in a state hospital, private hospitals, and several other hospitals for my bipolar 1. I have learned a lot about the mental health system here in my state.

I first became aware of WRAP in September of 2001 when the mental health center had a two-day course on WRAP. I did attend both days and I received a certificate. I read the red WRAP book from cover-to-cover, but at this time I really didn't see how I could use it much in my life to help me deal with my bipolar 1.

Then in January, 2004, I started taking WRAP at our mental health center and I thought in much more detail how to use my WRAP for recovery and to keep me aware of how my mental illness was going. A case manager who took extra training on WRAP taught the class. Each time we went to the WRAP group, we had to do progress notes on what we had learned in that session, and the mental health center got a copy and so did those of us who were taking the WRAP, and so we had a blue note book to put these notes in for future use.

I was learning a new language to help me stay in recovery. I learned what a Daily Maintenance Plan was and how to work it in my life. My Daily Maintenance Plan taught me that there were certain things in my life that I needed to do each day to help me stay well. Some of these things are eat three balanced meals, drink at least eight glasses of water each day, do my daily devotions, read my Bible, talk to friends, and spend some time writing in my journal. I have also found that helping others and doing some type of volunteer work has been very good to work into my life.

Triggers are what have taught me to watch when my mental illness is just starting to do not very well. They also help me to look at what is going on in my life with relationships, anger, and the time of anniversaries of bad things that have been in my past. Triggers have also showed me what things set me off now in my life, and to better deal with them using my WRAP. Some of the triggers in my life now are losses, bad news, crisis, dealing with surgeries and blood tests, and loud noises. My WRAP gives me more confidence to overcome my triggers and to "take a break" and regroup and break the triggers down into small details that I can manage easier and have less stress.

The Early Warning Signs are conditions that let me know I should start talking to my case manager, therapist, or psychiatrist. They also let me know that my mental illness isn't doing okay, especially my depression part of my bipolar 1. In the Early Warning Signs, sometimes I don't always see what is going on and it takes the case manager or therapist to alert me that I need to start looking at my WRAP. Both the case manager and therapist at different times have told me to get my WRAP out and start looking at it, and see what changes in my life right then that my WRAP could help with, and improve my life back to recovery. Because I have taken their advice, I have stopped my situation before it had become a full-blown crisis problem. My WRAP also gets me talking again to the case manager, therapist, or doctor, because sometimes I get angry at them.

Again, I go back to my journaling as help to self-reflect as to what is going on in my life at the present time. My WRAP helps me to try to relax and do something that I enjoy, like my stamp collection or working in my garden. This helps me to get a handle on things when I have Early Warning Signs.

Even when I try really hard with my mental illness, things can get worse and break down, which puts me close to a crisis stage. Some of my systems that let me know that things aren't going well are that I stay in bed too much, suicidal thoughts, irrational thoughts, isolating, racing thoughts, a lot of anger, and poor personal hygiene. Things that I use with my WRAP are to make sure my doctor and therapist know what is happening, use my daily maintenance, play, get my symptoms under control by positive self talk, journaling for fifteen minutes, and do something fun. I also try to call friends and talk and write letters and notes to special people in my life that understand my mental illness.

I just have been in a recent depression state of my bipolar 1. I couldn't see that the anger I had toward a lot of people was making my life miserable. The doctor and I tried a medicine change and that really didn't help much. Everything that could go wrong in my life did, especially with my relationships with others. I didn't use my WRAP as I should have. If I had, I could maybe have gotten over my depression sooner. My therapist said in one of my sessions with her, "Have you been using your WRAP?" I had to be honest with her and I said, "No." Even my therapist knew that WRAP could help me, if I could just take the effort to get the WRAP red book out and blue note book, and start seeing again what the triggers had been. I then could have seen how that crisis could be helped by working my WRAP.

Sometimes I have to learn the hard way, and I need to be reminded to look at my red WRAP book and reread again what I have underlined, and apply it to my present situation, and keep doing that until it becomes second nature for me to do. The road to recovery is a hard one for most of us who are mentally ill, and WRAP is there to help us remain in our recovery, even though things in life may upset us and go wrong.

I know I need my WRAP Crisis Planning when I cry over small things, can't make simple decisions, neglect personal hygiene, isolate myself from family and friends, have extreme mood swings, self-destructive behavior, and suicidal thoughts worse than in my Early Warning Signs.

The WRAP Crisis Plan gives me supporters who take over in my life when I can no longer take care of my self. My supporters are family members, friends, case manager, therapist, doctor, and religious leader. Each of these persons has specific duties to do for me when I am in crisis. They can also help give me support and see if a hospitalization is necessary. I could stay at home with people checking or staying with me, or go to attend care for a few days and get the care to help me get doing better, and see that the crisis has let up or will soon pass. In the WRAP, my oldest sister's name is there, because she has my power-of-attorney.

My WRAP has taught me to keep an up-to-date listing of all medications, how often I take them, how much I take, when I take them, and numbers of the person who is my oldest sister to contact if I am in an accident or can't talk. I carry a piece of paper in my billfold with most of this information on it. I do try to keep the information up to date. In my WRAP, there is also a place for medicines that I have allergies to, and I have referred back to my WRAP for this information. I can easily get it if I am in need of it in a crisis.

I have also stated in my WRAP Crisis Plan what hospitals I would care to go to and those which I wouldn't. I have also put in my WRAP which treatments I want and don't want. I don't want electric shock, being in restraints or to be put in a half way house. I would consider a medicine change as needed, case management, attendant care, and therapy. I have had some bad treatments while I was hospitalized and most of them are written above. All of us who are mentally ill have our horror memories.

I also have a Post Crisis Plan which I haven't had to use yet in my WRAP notebook. I have written in my WRAP Post Crisis Plan who I want to help me when I come home from being hospitalized. I know who in the community I want help from, what services I desire, who will provide these services and the other details that need to be taken care of at the time I come home. I have the names of these services and phone numbers when I need them.

I have these things written out in the Post Crisis Plan, but most of it will have to wait until the situation arises.

My last hospitalization was in 2002 at the state hospital and a general hospital. Since then I have taken WRAP at my mental health center. It took from about January 2004 to April 2004. This time span gave me more time to think about things that were of interest to me to put in my WRAP and to update it when I needed to do so. WRAP has helped me to look at my bipolar 1 and know that with the WRAP that I can stay in recovery better. I know in the future I will try to use my WRAP more often when problems do come, to help me stay more stable and to enjoy my life more with family and friends. My WRAP will give me the encouragement, if things do go wrong, to set me back on the road to stay in recovery. I am really thankful that I have my WRAP and I can go to it any time if I feel some triggers getting in, or just to do my daily maintenance plan. 🐦

26

In the late 1980s when I was in my late thirties I received the greatest gifts of my life.

All through my childhood I grew up feeling I was different. My family acted differently than my few friends' families did. I was taught about "family secrets," and Mom needed to take medicine so she wasn't sad all the time. Dad resorted to his evening ritual of gin and tonic and/or beer. At that time there were big institutions in my state and there was a constant threat over me that if I couldn't be socially appropriate, I could be sent to one. As time passed I began to feel fear and anxiety, I cried a lot and just wanted to isolate. Going to school caused me to become physically ill. I learned to tolerate this and learned skills to perform the way I thought people wanted me to. I was a quiet person that isolated myself and made sure I did what I thought people wanted of me to escape the threat of institutionalization. These skills got me through high school and into the employment field.

I met the man of my dreams and married. Two years later I was blessed with a son. However, throughout the pregnancy and after birth we had to deal with the fact that our son had disabilities. My husband became disabled. I took back my role as survivor and caretaker, as well as the wage earner.

In 1985 I lost my husband to a freak accident in our yard. A car he was working on fell on him, killing him instantly. I became very deeply depressed. My only saving graces were my son and God. I put on my "I'm okay" mask and started life over. I attended college and got my bachelor's degree in therapeutic recreation. I went to work at an institution for children who were behaviorally challenged, some of whom had severe physical disabilities and were receiving hospice care. Great place for a person with manic depression to work. Sadness was perceived as normal because of the many challenges I dealt with daily. However, I needed energy to perform the duties, and so mania was seen as "high energy." I learned about masks and the need to use them to survive.

This program was closed in the late 1980s. I heard of a pilot program through the state to provide scholarships to peers who would like to get masters degrees. I signed up and was accepted. After two years I needed to do an internship, and because of my peer history it was hard to find a place. A peer clubhouse accepted me. At the same time the state was offering a pilot project for training in recovery. The idea was to have my clubhouse as a site. I was to be a site coordinator. The trainer was Mary Ellen Copeland. Through five intensive eight-hour training days I learned I wasn't alone and I didn't need to hide behind masks. I started using the training faithfully for my own recovery.

Next, there was a training offered by the state to train peers to teach the recovery materials to others. Again I was accepted and became a recovery trainer. I also became familiar with a statewide peer run program. I interviewed and was hired as the recovery education coordinator for the state. I had never been outside of my state unless it was in a car and then only nearby areas. I quickly learned the art of traveling, and, fortunately, Mary Ellen Copeland was at most of the conferences, so there was a familiar face. In our state a group of peers got together with Mary Ellen and they designed the Wellness Recovery Action Plan (WRAP). People were trained in this model, and, as many know, it is still used today.

After being at the state organization for two years I was selected to replace our existing executive director. I was fortunate in the fact he had taught me about the organization and was a peer role model for me.

I feel my life was guided by my Divine Master whom I choose to call God. The introduction to the peer world gave me the experience of peer support and its value. Education is a tool that I continue to use. However, the greatest gift to me was the opportunity to meet Mary Ellen and have the opportunity to work with her on so many projects.

Am I recovered? I would say no, but with my WRAP I can see my early warning signs, or peers that know me may give me a gentle reminder to take a break and rejuvenate before I burnout. I recognize anniversary dates and holidays and find things that are positive to do so that I don't relapse. I also give myself permission to make mistakes and learn from them, as that is part of growing. ❧

27

There is a Buddhist proverb that says, "When the student is ready, the teacher will appear." This is how Mary Ellen Copeland and many other people associated with mental health recovery came into my life in 1996. A friend talked me into attending an hour-long talk that Mary Ellen was giving as part of "May is Mental Health Month" activities sponsored somehow by one of the state agencies in Rhode Island. The talk was at a hotel near where I live. I never would have gone if it weren't for the encouragement of a friend who has a daughter with bipolar disorder and addiction problems.

I was diagnosed with bipolar disorder in April of 1995. The diagnosis was not really a surprise but it scared me and I felt like my life had been turned upside down. I had been diagnosed with major depression over ten years earlier, given a variety of different diagnoses as the years went by, but 1995 was the first time I sought the help of a psychiatrist and considered medication. I needed more help than I was getting from psychotherapy alone. I was experiencing stretches lasting weeks at a time when I could not get adequate sleep. Racing thoughts, agitation, and physical sensitivity made it painful for me to even have someone brush up against me in a hallway. At night I was tired but when I went to bed thoughts exploded in my mind from everywhere. At times I felt like someone was playing a slide show in my mind that I couldn't stop. When I tried to sleep it often felt like I was the deer caught in the headlights, but the intensity was closer to the spotlights on an airport runway. I wound up on the couch most nights, watching re-runs on Nick-At-Nite while my husband slept. Around the time the sun came up I'd manage to sleep for an hour or two. I still had to get up and go to work. I became progressively more ragged. Somehow I was still functioning.

In spite of having some symptoms of mania, I was fearful and depressed. Along with the racing thoughts I began to have perception problems. People seemed to be talking very fast. I had to concentrate very hard to understand what they were saying. Sometimes I repeated the sound in my mind and slowed it down to interpret it. If a conversation was moving too fast, I couldn't understand it at all and would ask people to repeat what they had said. Or I would nod as if I understood and hope they would stop talking because everything just seemed to make my head hurt. I felt like I was constantly in a fog. I repeated things back to people to be sure I had understood what they said. Some days it was like living in a Charlie Brown TV special where people sounded like the cartoon parents until I replayed them in my mind. It was hard, time-consuming, and energy-consuming. Speaking was equally draining for me. The only part of me that worked well for communication was typing or writing and reading. Because that is the mode that I did much of my work in, I managed to continue to function reasonably well and manage the symptoms of my illness for quite a while. But I was leading a team of engineers doing some very difficult work. The day I went into work and found myself unable to read a technical document because I could not interpret the letters on the page, I knew I needed more help.

I was about a year into my treatment under the care of a psychiatrist the night I went to Mary Ellen's talk. The treatment was not going well. My psychiatrist got me past the problem of not sleeping with medication, but his solution to all of my problems seemed to be sedating me out of my misery. What I had learned in a year of psychiatric treatment for bipolar disorder seemed to be that I would never have my life back as I had known it. If anything, I was more depressed than I had been a year before. I was also now unable to function well enough to work and was on medical leave from my job. I was certainly open to hearing a different message.

The message was a surprise. Here was someone telling me that I could recover. This woman standing in the front of the room was some-one like me. Her story was something I could relate to. She was saying things that resonated deeply and for the first time in a year, I felt a ray of light and a sense of hope. Mary Ellen was scheduled to give two more talks in Rhode Island over the next two days. Both talks were longer workshops and they were on the other side of the state in a hospital that I'd never been to. I had no idea where it was and I hadn't ventured any-where on my own in weeks. I found it anyway. Those of you who know Rhode Island are probably laughing at the idea of "the other side of the state" and how far that is. For those of you unfamiliar with Rhode Is-land, the entire state is maybe 30 miles wide and 40 miles north to south. At the time, it took a lot for me to go very far on my own.

I think her workshop the next day was three hours. The one on Saturday that I brought my husband to was all day. I may have been the only person who showed up all three days and for that reason, I know I stood out. I also tend to sit towards the front of rooms out of habit, and my personality makes me show up prepared to take notes. Something about hearing the same message over three days, explained more fully each time, helped it get through to me. I left those three days with a sense of hope that I had not had in a long time. On the third day of Mary Ellen's talks, she mentioned that there might be a workshop at Trinity College that summer. I gave her information for getting in touch with me and eventually found my way to Vermont.

By the time summer rolled around, I was so deeply depressed that I went to the workshop with a mindset that I was going to really put myself out there and do what I needed to do to help myself. I was pretty much at the end of my rope. I remember the week as providing me with support and tools I needed to get started on the right path. WRAP was not yet a term that existed, but all of the elements were there. When I came home after that workshop, I slowly started taking baby steps to-ward getting back on track. I have been in touch with Mary Ellen pe-riodically since then. My first major step was finding a decent psychia-trist, one with the skills needed to treat my illness. I tried a different one locally and had some initial improvement. I returned to work, only to have another setback. Back I went to Mary Ellen's work, not yet called WRAP, and another workshop, still trying to pull myself together. Hope was a key element in what was happening in my life. Building a support system was gradually happening. I turned to the internet for help in finding yet another psychiatrist.

There is a site that lists the top psychopharmacologists in the United States. One of them lives near me but does not see patients. He teaches at Tufts University and Brown University. I asked my husband to call him and see if he would be willing to see me, go over my history and recommend someone who might be able to treat me. The doctor agreed to see me for a consulting fee. He recommended three psychiatrists in my area, all with advanced training in psychopharmacology. One of the three accepted my insurance. He's been my psychiatrist since then. I had to wait seven weeks for the initial appointment, which seemed like an eternity, but it was worth it. What followed was a couple of years of trial and error, tweaking medication until we found a working combination of medication that has me feeling really decent most of the time.

Over the same time period, I found other ways to keep my focus on my recovery. One opportunity came during a workshop in Vermont when, with a few keystrokes, the first mental health recovery e-group came into existence. I am still one of the moderators of what is now mental-health-recovery@yahoogroups.com, where people can come for support on anything related to WRAP. The ongoing presence of email and support from this list keeps WRAP present in my daily life and keeps a focus for me on what's important to maintaining my well-being. Moderating is a small contribution back to the community for the help I've been given.

Other things I've found that I might have missed without WRAP include a more holistic approach to life. Learning to do all of the simple parts of self-care, including eating right, making sure I get enough sleep, exercising, planning some fun into my days, and maintaining and making new relationships with friends took some work for me. The changes did not occur overnight, but they did occur. Each little step, like an hour-long talk with a friend, can be the first step toward a happier life. ✍

So there you have it. Lots of stories about how WRAP has worked for people, in many instances transforming their lives.

In all of my pleas for stories, I got only one story from a person who said WRAP didn't help. It is as follows:

28

When I got sick, my friends and family, and special people who work in organizations and the mental health system, helped by mentioning my concerns at meetings. They helped work out our communication breakdowns and misunderstandings. They helped improve healthier situations. They helped write and edit my interview of the story of my experiences.

Newsletters, people, organizations, volunteers, and friends help that way. I have helpful friends out of state and in state. My family is out of state; when I get a chance to go away to visit and see family and friends, I go away and have fun, educational, interesting opportunities.

I needed help when I had many misunderstandings accumulate in the mental health system. I got very physically sick and burned out from the mental health system. I spend a lot of time alone in the city where I live. I saw people sometimes downtown; when I didn't see people, I lost hope. It was an unhealthy situation.

The situation improved so much because one person helped so much and gave me so much hope. She helped give me hope that things would get better. She helped when I go places, she taught me to look for a lot of detail. I enjoy having fun, seeing pretty sights, and taking vacations.

When I was past my limits, I felt afraid, felt uncomfortable, afraid of the mental health system when things did not get resolved. I suffered great trouble receiving services in this state. If my friend would help me and give me more time, I trust her. She has helped me so much. If there is more education, training, advocacy and assistance and support, help at meetings and groups, programs, accommodations to help with communication resolving misunderstandings and communication breakdowns with the mental health systems, this would be good. More education, training, advocacy, and assistance would prevent stress from accumulating and getting out of control and ending up in a crisis of life threatening danger.

My health went down the tubes; I got dizzy and passed out. My health problems include chronic bronchitis, sinus and respiratory burn out. For a long time I got help from my friend. She had more time to help. I find her so helpful.

If there were better grievance procedures in this mental health system, then things would not be neglected to the point of a serious crisis before anyone ever notices. And if clients and staff of this mental health system, and staff and board members of this state's agency of protection and advocacy were educated, there would be so much better understanding of different experiences and different ways of expressing and doing things. If my friend had more time to help, she'd help me. I trust her, and we developed a very helpful long-time relationship.

When I was in deep serious trouble, I needed help. I lost hope, felt afraid, overwhelmed, past my limits, overextended, physically sick, and burned-out from not knowing where to find help. I went to an agency to try to find help. A friend there helped me.

I have suffered devastating pain caused by the mental health system. I have isolated feelings. I feel isolated at meetings in this mental health system when there are so many misunderstandings in this mental health system.

Yes, I did try WRAP, but it did not work out too well, so I stopped it.

I do things that bring me happiness, healing. I did enjoy conventions and conferences. I enjoy out-of-state ones most. I feel better if I get more rest and do things. I am happy to do it. It helps much more.

I feel sad times over missing a friend that passed away, gone, and missing friends that live far away. I have some happy times. I feel sad when a lot of people in this mental health system end up not being good friends or were good friends once and we drifted apart. I had to withdraw from some people when I was hurt. The mental health system is spread too thin. They did not understand a lot.

A WRAP plan could only work if someone can know and feel hope. It was helpful when we did WRAP at the church. But now it's no longer helpful because they do not let me do it my way. The WRAP plan was helpful when let me do it my way. ❧

WRAP Around the World

It is exciting to me that WRAP, this simple self-help recovery process, and the values and ethics we espouse, have made their way around the world, supporting people whose lives are so different from the people who developed WRAP and use it in the United States. Following are stories from people from various countries and cultures, who were able to use WRAP, and/or the values and ethics that surround it, to work in powerful and effective ways on their recovery and on making their lives the way they want them to be. However, please note that some things in these narratives do not fully reflect the values and ethics associated with WRAP. But I feel the stories are too important to exclude, and, in considering them, we must understand their unique cultural perspective.

1

My Recovery Experience

In the 1980s, I owned my own factory in Hong Kong with over a thousand workers under my management. Because of the intensive work pressure, I could not live my normal life. I had problems with a bad appetite and sleep. I had extremely persistent feelings of high anxiety and was diagnosed with an anxiety disorder. The doctor in Hong Kong suggested I move to a different living environment. Therefore, my whole family migrated to New Zealand in 1991. Soon after that, my husband returned to Hong Kong for the business while I stayed alone in New Zealand with our newborn child. At that time, I lived a relaxed and leisurely life with no work pressure. I often spent time relaxing with friends all day long. Unfortunately, one day in 1997, I received a call from a bank in Hong Kong regarding my debts. By that time I finally realized that my husband had been indulging in gambling and played away all our properties. Upon hearing that, I suddenly collapsed and returned to Hong Kong with my child. I sold out my properties and brought my husband back to New Zealand. But my husband did not make any changes. He still gambled. That led me into an extreme tension and anxiety.

From 1999 on, I suffered heavy insomnia, melancholy, being fidgety, and always wanting to commit suicide. My GP suggested I see a psychiatrist. I was very angry with his words and didn't think I had a mental disease. I rebutted him, "How could I have a mental disease?" Based on Chinese cultural values, if somebody was diagnosed with mental illness it was a big stigma. Even some professional medical staff often misunderstood mental disease and discriminated against the mental patients. I still remember that once a Chinese doctor asked me directly: "You have mental disease, once you get unwell, would you abuse somebody?" Just because of lack of the basic knowledge on mental disease, I firmly denied the fact that I was a mental disease patient.

Afterwards, I began to see a Chinese psychiatrist, and he introduced me to a community support worker from Te Korowai Aroha (TKA). At the beginning I was hostile to her and refused to communicate. When I was upset, she listened to me very patiently, and communicated with me. The Chinese community worker was very kind to help me apply for government welfare, and accompanied me to the government authorities for negotiating. She regularly visited me at home, encouraged me to take part in the activities held by the Boai She. I used to be the team leader of the Care Team in Boai She. As time went on, I was impressed by her dedication, trusted her, and we established a good relationship.

Now, I have basically gotten well and do not receive the services from TKA. In reviewing my recovery experiences, I think the Chinese Boai She and the Wellness Recovery Action Planning (WRAP) have played the most important function to me.

At first, the most difficult thing for Chinese people who have been dealing with psychiatric symptoms is to help them overcome their own stigma and to eliminate their fear of mental disorders. The Chinese Boai She is an important social support resource to help them walk out of the shadow of the disease. In BoAi She, members with the same background can share struggles and achievements and support each other. Furthermore, we have resolved to keep the insights, attitude and practical aids. I am one of the coordinators and the earliest members of the Chinese Boai She. I used to drive the new members for sightseeing. Taking my own sociable advantage, I am keen of helping others, which has enriched my aspiration to help my own recovery. Surely, as a mental health community service organisation, TKA has helped the Chinese Boai She with professional knowledge, consultation and management supervision, which have positively promoted the development of Boai She. I sincerely hope TKA could continuously support and guide it.

Secondly, the Wellness Recovery Action Planning has made a big contribution towards my recovery. By attending to the workshops, watching the educational videos, reading relevant articles and other resources, as well as communicating with and cooperating with the medical staff, I am aware of my own state of symptoms. Through a comprehensive range of study, I have gained a better understanding of schizophrenia and reduced my fears. With the support of the community support worker, based on my personal status, I established my goals and my detailed action planning to control my state and improve my quality of life.

Through learning the process of WRAP, I can predict serious symptoms, and can tackle a crisis situation. In 2003, I found my husband was gambling again. I could not control my emotions. I wanted to commit suicide and kill the whole family. Luckily, I had attended a recovery course, and have been aware of severe signs and crisis planning. So, at the right moment, I had made phone calls for help, stopped the tragedy from happening, and rescued my family and myself.

I would like to express gratitude to the community support worker for her helps, support and encouragement from TKA. Now, I live a normal positive life with my family. My recovery experiences illustrates that although we may have undergone psychological hurt and mental disease, we can still win over the diseases and live a happy, meaningful life. 🐦

2
My Experiences in Recovering from Mental Illness

I am from Mainland China. I migrated to New Zealand ten years ago when I was at the peak of my career in China. My employer and my family suggested I stay in China and keep my bright future, but my ex-wife was dreaming of going abroad. I also had a contradiction on my mind. On one side, I would like to go overseas to gain some broad sight, but on the other side, I worried about the life difficulties in another country due to my limited English. However, eventually I arrived in New Zealand in spite of these contradictions.

After arriving in Auckland, I had to start from scratch and nothing went well for me. I really found a big loss from the psychological perspectives due to the huge changes in language and culture. I worked at a restaurant with a friend's recommendation, but soon after, I could not tolerate the owner's abusive comments towards me and therefore I quit the job. I felt regret and anger about leaving my home country, and as a result, my marriage ended.

A few years later I got married again. But generally, I found I became timid and always felt that someone would hurt me. Simultaneously, I also suffered from insomnia and heard constant noises in my head. But I did not realize that there was something wrong with my mental health. Later, my wife urged me to see my family doctor who referred me to a psychiatric clinic. According to the assessment result, I was diagnosed with a serious depression and therefore the doctor requested me to take medications.

I was thrown into the deep end when the result came out. Chinese people, ourselves, had already suffered from ethnic prejudice in overseas, how even the mental illness as an addition? I must be thought as a "mad man" and suffer the prejudice in double. There would be not any hope in the future! The suffering from the mental illness and the coming poverty made me drop into the bottom of the life. I hid myself at home, did not dare to go out and did not wish to meet people, but only felt sorry about myself. In order to save face and avoid the concerns from my family, relatives and friends in China, I did not want them to know about my situation.

During these years, with the support services received from the doctor and Chinese Community Worker, and also the participation in the activities run by the Chinese patient support group, I have gained a very big improvement for my conditions and been able to lead a normal life as others do. About a few months ago, I started my full-time job from a company! Although my English is still very limited, I was quite admired by my employers because of my hard work and positive learning attitudes. My employers not only offer me extra bonus every week, but also encourage me to learn English and computing to undertake more important responsibilities.

My experiences in recovery from the mental illness can be summarized as following: We should reconcile ourselves to our situations. We should be content with our life no matter if we are poor or rich. If we always compare ourselves with others in terms of money and social status, we will always be unhappy with our own situations. Thus we will always be in a stressful state. We need to adjust ourselves from unhealthy thoughts and keep an open mind to be happy in whatever situation.

We need social and community supports. I took part in the Chinese-speaking support group Bo Ai She before I got the job. All the members there are in the same boat, so we did not worry about the discriminations from others when we got together. We can exchange our feelings and emotions there freely. Asian support workers in mental health service TKA also taught us the WRAP recovery plan so we could make our own recovery and relapse prevention plans.

Lastly, in the process of recovery, we should set up some practical goals. We should not expect to achieve some big goal in a short time, which might bring more stress to their still fragile mental system, but need to start from small goals that are easily reached, step-by-step. Thus our life will not be too stressful and our sickness can be controlled. ॐ

3
My Recovery Experience

It can be put back to 1999, when some strong disputes raised between my family and I, from which my nerve was badly damaged. My life started being chaotic, going from one nightmare to another one. Since then I could not go to sleep at night with a lot of imagination and angers in my mind. I was disappointed and hated everyone, and frequently I was preoccupied with death and intended to kill people around me. Soon, I was diagnosed as schizophrenic. Consequently, I was discriminated against by own community. I was sunk in despair and almost lost my belief in life. My conditions became worse and worse. In 2001, in order to get rid of that circumstance, I followed my son and settled down in New Zealand.

In October 2001, I went to a Mental Health Centre in Auckland for treatment. Now, I have generally got well and been able to take an active part in the society and family life. At present, I am one of the key members of Boai Group, which is a mutual aid community for Chinese mental illness patients in Auckland to get recovery. In addition, I participate in some voluntary work in my church. However, on the basis of my own experience of recovery, there are a few points I would like to conclude as the following:

Firstly, the support and services provided by the health care providers and social welfare department are very important.

When I first arrived at New Zealand, I got benefits support from Work and Income. The case manager noticed my behavior was somewhat abnormal, and therefore referred me to Te Korowai Aroha (TKA), and I got remarkable assistance and appropriate cultural support from the Chinese community support worker. The Chinese community workers from TKA helped me communicate with the local mental health centre to get the psychiatrist, also the centre offered me interpreting services. All the services I received were free of charge. Due to my Kiwi psychiatrist, the community workers had accompanied me for the medical treatment and had helped me a lot on language and cultural communication. Slowly but obviously I got better and stronger, and then I was transferred to a nearby GP. At the early stage, my family doctor did not treat me well. The community support worker from TKA therefore did a lot of work on explanation and communication, and helped my GP understand the special cultural background and features of Chinese patients. Now my GP is very nice to me. However, I was helped and supported by a TKA community support worker through regularly home visiting or greetings over phone. In terms of her endeavor, I was able to access the social and medical resources and mainstream culture in New Zealand. The most important is, TKA utilizes the "strengths method" to help me re-established my self-esteem and make me believe that I can overcome the disease eventually.

Second, the mutual aid within the community is also very important. In New Zealand, due to language and cultural obstacles, in particularly, without any relatives around (my son left to go back to China later), my solitude doubled, so I especially need social and cultural support from the community. Through the introduction of TKA Chinese community worker, I have enjoyed in the Chinese Mental Illness Recovery Group-"Boai She", which intensely contributed to my recovery. In Boai She, I understood and obtained the knowledge of mental illness prevention and recovery through some workshops and training programs run by the medical professionals. We also have some classes for English, Tai Chi and some other relaxing treatments. It is extremely effective for us to share our recovery experiences and encourage and support each other. Since I joined the Boai She, I have been always insistently and actively participate in the activities in any kind. "In helping others, I have been actively taking part in its activities held by the Boai She".

In addition, Wellness Recovery Action Planning (WRAP) has brought me huge effects during my recovery process. According to the direction of WRAP, I wrote a Crisis Plan to deal with urgent cases. I would tell the people who live with me about some important issues, e.g. identifications, important documents (Bank Card, the place to save money), contact details for my family doctor and psychiatrist, etc. I try to create a good environment for living, so that if I am sick, I can recover sooner. If feel well, I will follow the requirements of my WRAP Daily Maintenance Plan to learn how to control my symptoms.

Now, I can not only take good care of myself, but also help others in the church. I feel privileged that I can live in New Zealand; I like it because it is my home. ๕๖

4

My Roads to Recovery

I migrated to New Zealand in the early 1970's under the marriage category. My husband was a New Zealand born Chinese. After I arrived in New Zealand, we resided in another city out of Auckland. My husband was working for a company as a manager at that time.

My first child died in an accident when he was about 4 years old. The loss of my son was a big shock to me. Then, probably due to my being married with a close relative, my second and third children were born with the problems of intellectual disability. This was another big shock to my mental state. And more seriously, because of my children's conditions, my family and I were discriminated against by some people, especially those people who were close to us. Some of my friends even called my children idiots.

Both the family tragedies and the discriminations from others caused the collapse of my mental health and I often had the thoughts of committing suicide. In 1992, I was diagnosed with the serious depression.

At that time there was no Mandarin or Cantonese speaking psychiatrist in the city I lived in, and I had communication difficulties in getting help from the psychiatrist. So after I had got sick, a friend of mine suggested to me to go up to Auckland to see a psychiatrist who is from

Hong Kong. In a few years before 2000, I went up to Auckland twice a year to visit the psychiatrist. In 2000, our family moved to Auckland for the sake of my mental health.

Now I have basically recovered from my conditions and am actively involved in the community and family life. I am the liaison person for the Chinese mental health support group 'Bo Ai She' and a volunteer worker for a public library in Auckland at the moment. My personal experiences in recovery from the mental illness are as follows:

Firstly, in order to recover as early as possible we should be full of love in our hearts towards others. I think that caring for other people and offering help to the people in need are not only good for them but also very conducive to our own health. By helping others we can recognize our own value as a human being in the community, improve our self-confidence and develop a comprehensive life, so that we will not only concentrate on our own mental problems.

After I finished my own job in 1998, I started to work for a rest home as a volunteer. Because of my limited English, I decided to work in the kitchen and brought my kitchen hand skills into full play. My work was highly admired by the elderly people in this rest home. Through this work I felt I was a useful person rather than an incapable one in the society. Now I am still doing voluntary work for the Bo Ai She and the library. Last year I was awarded a volunteer reward in Auckland.

Secondly, seeking for community support. You can imagine how difficult it will be for a mentally ill person living in a foreign country without knowing its language. In order to recover as early as possible, we should seek for the help and support from the communities with the same cultural background. For the Chinese speaking people living in New Zealand, especially in Auckland, they are very luck now because we not only have got the mental professionals who can speak our languages, but also there are some Chinese mental heath support groups. Furthermore, nowadays the mainstream mental health service providers are recruiting more and more Asian Community Support Workers. Over the last couple of years I myself have received huge support from Asian

Community Support workers in NGO mental health service provider TKA. Through learning the WRAP recovery action plan organized by TKA, I made my own recovery plan and relapse plan (WRAP) and I also met some friends through this activity. We support and help with each other.

In addition, with the help of the Asian Support Worker in TKA, we established a mentally ill patient support group Bo Ai She two years ago. People in Bo Ai She also offer me a lot of support during the process of my recovery. In Bo Ai She, we learn and practice Tai Chi, yoga and some other relaxing therapies. We share our feelings and recovery experiences with each other. I think that for a person with mental illness, the support from his or her own communities sometimes are more effective in term of recovery, since this kind of supports are tend to be more culturally appropriate.

Thirdly, we need spiritual support. Personal religion is also conducive to the recovery since it can offer us with spiritual support. I used to go to the church to pray to and worship God. At present, due to some reasons I do not go to the church anymore but whenever I feel depressed I still pray to God and ask for His blessings.

In summary, I would say to everyone who has got mentally illnesses that each of us has our own strengths and potentials. We can recover if we can identify these strengths and fully make use of them. ॐ

5

Great Britain

I was diagnosed four years ago with depression and anxiety disorder. I had a very good doctor who realized I had problems and got me the help I needed. I owe a lot to him for not giving up on me. This was the best thing that happened to me after going to groups on assertiveness and self esteem. It was suggested I take a course where we worked towards making a crisis plan. This I have since learned is also called a WRAP. This has been very good for me as it helps me identify things that make me happy and contented. These include going on walks, being involved in conservation groups and being out in the open. It also has helped to recognize the triggers of things that make me feel suicidal and feeling low, these being particularly difficult when I feel isolated and feeling a failure and unable to cope. This understanding has helped me to work out a wellness kit, to help me through the bad times. I have recently become a volunteer with Rethink and have done another WRAP, and have updated and revisited what worked for me. I have made sure my doctor and C.P.N. know my wishes, in the likelihood that I would not be able to request them myself. Having a WRAP has helped me get on with my life, and cope with good and bad days. I would recommend that everyone has one.

6

How WRAP has Changed My Life

In 1998, when I received the diagnosis of manic depression I was at first relieved. At last it was official, and I thought that I would now be able to "manage" my illness with the help of lithium. I had an "excuse" for spending too much, not wanting to sleep, being slightly "naughty"—I had an illness that I could not control and other people would have to look after me!

I was devastated when I was forced to retire from my teaching job, which I loved. I very soon realized that I was not going to let others take control of my life. Luckily, I was able to attend a day-long presentation on Recovery and WRAP in 2000, where Mary Ellen Copeland introduced the plan which is now my lifeline. I attended courses in Birmingham and Vermont, USA, and have completely turned my life around, thanks to the training and a lot of hard work and determination.

I have so much improved my control of my illness that my psychiatrist, who has never seen me ill, has decided I was misdiagnosed (how wrong she is), and has withdrawn all my mental health support! My doctor, who treated me some years ago when I was very manic, also cannot believe the change in me now and, again the stigma, thinks I cannot be "one of them."

I am now using my WRAP to stay alive, and, as well as I can be, focused on what is happening to me and what I need to do each day to keep myself well. This is not easy, as I am now not only dealing with mental illness, but severe physical illness, probably multiple sclerosis, and living alone for the first time ever. I am now 56, recovering from the trauma of an abusive marriage, which I have had to leave after 33 years, and getting over the death of my mother recently.

I have learned so many new Wellness Tools, especially peer counseling, relaxation, ways of slowing down, of calming down, indeed, amazing to people who know me, of actually going to bed and sleeping or relaxing when I am hit by the fatigue which is a part of the physical illness.

In spite of all I have had to face in the last year, I now count myself as lucky to be alive each day, and hope to live long enough to see my grandchildren, to write my book, to fight the stigma, to teach WRAP to others, but most of all I am confident that I can deal with it all, thanks to my WRAP plan. 🐦

7

Great Britain

WRAP has been invaluable to me, although I've never done a course or used that term before. What I have done is to assimilate "The Depression Workbook" and "Living without Depression and Manic Depression." My life has been transformed.

I have manic depression; my pattern is to become manic, which, on four occasions, led to psychosis and sectioning. Each time, after I had slept, I recovered quickly, left the hospital, and got on with my life, refusing to address what was going on. My husband and I thought manic depression meant you got manic then depressed. That wasn't me.

My last, most public sectioning was in 1998. I realized I was in danger of losing my husband and damaging my children. I started to research and found I was a type who gets manic and not depressed. My world then fell apart for a time as I struggled with who I really was and what it meant. Enter Mary Ellen. I developed my own plan for wellness based around her work. I realized I had to change aspects of my life and accept my vulnerability and at times learn to say, "my judgment is not very good at the moment" and retreat from life. I dated my entries in the workbooks and unwittingly developed both a record of my progress and the most valuable tool I could use in my recovery.

Eight years on I still have episodes, but I manage them, I haven't been hospitalized, I haven't tipped over into psychosis and I take medication only if I need to. My psychiatrist recently discharged me (I went twice a year to see her) because she felt I was so well, but reassured me that if I need her or her team they are there for me.

So, what is my Wellness Recovery Action Plan? Firstly, I insisted on seeing the same consultants each time I went to the mental health unit so I could build up a relationship with them and I learned as much as I could about the condition. I then developed hobbies that would ground me: singing, keeping fit, playing the piano and horseback riding. I understood that as I lacked the mechanism most people have which lets them know that they are over-doing it, I would have to rely on greater self-awareness and feed-back from a few special friends, and most importantly, my husband. I learned what my triggers are and what early behaviors indicate I may be becoming manic. I learned about distorted thinking and challenged myself to stop my thought processes from escalating wildly. When I am in what I call the "foothills of mania", I learned to put the brakes on my life, to avoid over-stimulating myself. I was initially extremely cautious in what I would or wouldn't do, but as I learned my triggers and controls, I gained in confidence and lost the fear. For example, I planned to do less at potentially stressful times, ensuring I slept well. I consciously dropped "fair weather" and stressful friends who drained me. I ran a self-help group funded by the local health authority for five years and learned and shared a lot about the condition. I used my workbook each time I recognized the initial signs of mania and photocopied the blank schedules for a person experiencing mania, which I used to remind myself how to cope. I learned humility, and although at first I felt the manic depression was a blot on my life, I now feel I am a more compassionate, understanding person and the path down which I have been forced is just a different one. My husband and I have developed incredible closeness, understanding and trust, and both of us have grown emotionally to meet the challenges of manic depression. My daughters have been brought up with a greater awareness of what constitutes good health.

My Wellness Recovery Action Plan supports me when I'm well, when I'm becoming ill and when I'm in recovery from an episode. I have built up a bank of ideas how to calm myself down, which I've added to my list. Some are so simple, e.g. walking up and down barefoot in a hot bath, working in the yard with my horse, and getting my husband to give me a massage.

Until recently I managed by taking sleeping pills at night and forcing myself to stay centered during the day, but in my last episode I tried a few days on a medication and found I didn't have to work so hard. I know what will increase and decrease my mood instability and when I work, I work only part time and I always put my mental health first. A typical entry for my workbook is:

Action you can take to keep mania under control:

- 🐦 Bed
- 🐦 Talk to no one
- 🐦 Don't answer the door or phone
- 🐦 Play the piano
- 🐦 Sit in steam bath
- 🐦 Have a bubble bath
- 🐦 Paint my nails
- 🐦 Tidy my bedroom and kitchen, taking on small tasks
- 🐦 Do some stretching exercises

The various aspects of WRAP, e.g. diet, exercise, support groups, are so comprehensive that I feel I will never run out of ways of exploring and learning to deal with mania. I asked my husband as I was writing this what he thinks of my progress and he said he feels I can now "hold my own" against the illness. I have never taken mood stabilizers so since

1998 I have been learning and developing strategies for living with manic depression. I feel I am more like my old self these days, spontaneous, funny, and able to enjoy a rich and varied life. Most importantly, what was a man-eating tiger hiding in the undergrowth waiting to pounce on me and wreck havoc in my life, is now a yappy little dog that occasionally tries to nip my ankles, but to whom, in order to protect myself, I can administer a swift effective kick. This is thanks to WRAP and to all the people who made it possible. 🦢

8
My Use of a WRAP Plan

I have special use and need a WRAP Plan because my care is provided for me by a special team of alternative therapists (19 in total). I can freely access any of them, but a plan of work was very important to link them all together. I have a psychiatrist but she allows and understands the choice I have made to be looked after by my alternative therapy team. My biggest sadness is that the direct payment system does not allow me to claim for reimbursable money to the therapy centre for services and they care for me for free. To do this for me and a few others, they have to continually fundraise. In return I give some voluntary time to the centre on reception as much and as often as I can or it is needed. Over 12 of us do this work voluntarily on reception, to thank them for the continuing care. It's an excellent model and firmly sits within the recovery models and in social inclusion and empowering and valuing people and human rights and disability acts.

It is a perfect way because our self-esteem and confidence is built up and there is always someone on hand to address our changing moods and needs while we are on and off the premises. Both physical and mental needs are firmly addressed. The Manager at the centre is a counselor and is firmly entrenched in WRAP planning and IN MY TOOLBOX. They have taught me and enabled me to put items into my toolbox, giving me lots of free training and introducing me to all types of therapy and techniques for my WRAP toolbox. Therefore I feel very well most of the time, and they can all see and help me should I "blip" sooner rather than later. I have been able to just chill with them and escape with them. They have given me access and permission night or day to access them by phone and have been available in the middle of the night. If I have had a problem they sit with me and see me through a particular bad patch. I have been taken on a canal boat they own for a wonderful relaxing weekend that made me feel recovered.

I am continually grateful, for the WRAP plan is well understood and firmly used by them and myself, thus enabling my family not to have to worry about my wellbeing. I have been privileged to become a WRAP Trainer, and look forward to being part of a bigger team soon so there is more help and experience in taking it forward.

My WRAP is probably very different and very special. Because of financial restraints, the therapy centre cannot provide this amount of coverage for many, but I am very lucky that I can be strongly supported so I can help as many people with their illness/ wellness and WRAP plans as possible, and manage the huge amount of Service User involvement active in my area.

I have a lot of personal struggles, as well as trying to be good at service user involvement, and, thankfully, my care and attention to my WRAP allows me to recognize my triggers or potential triggers and do something to head them off before they debilitate me.

The Centre allows me to be part of projects that help others in the community and allows me to freely use their premises to run the Manic Depression Fellowship Self Help Group. It is supporting me to help the people I come in contact with, and allowing me a quiet place to talk to people if they need advice, and going on to help them at the centre with access to treatments. I am thoroughly delighted that I can become a part of so many people's recovery plans, by encouraging them to seek out tools for their own toolboxes, because of the information and help I myself have been given, and thrilled to be a part not only of people on the mental health register's recovery, but part of early signs of depression through family and relationship problems.

A group of ten of the therapists and patients are walking the Camino in a few weeks, covering a sponsored passage of 144 miles, to raise funds for the ongoing work of the community. Those of us like me who cannot go on the walk are going along to the airport as they depart and arrive back and are keeping the centre afloat in their absence. The Walkers span a wide range of ages: two teenagers who have been brought back from the brink of drug and alcohol abuse, and therapists in age ranges from 30s to 60s, and physically recovered clients who have come back from the brink of very serious car accidents. All are setting off and walking the camino and on their return they will produce a book because along with sponsorship, sponsors have been allowed to dedicate a kilometer of the walk to someone either living or in memory. These dedications will be celebrated on the return in the book with mapping and photographs and everyone's kilometer will be celebrated in the book and recorded for posterity. And they are doing it to raise the money to include more people like me in a care package which will include a WRAP plan if the client wishes. Myself and my fellow WRAP trainers will be brought in when someone is identified by the staff with a willingness to work in the WRAP way, but in a subtle way all the therapy staff work with recovery and WRAP firmly fixed. Nine thousand pounds will be the target and this is hoped will pick up the number of clients that are identified in the system now and in the future year. The number of mentally ill is rising all the time, as well as victims of crime, abuse and personal trauma. A WRAP plan is relevant to all these groups because they all have to get from the place they find themselves now, either in wellness this week or trauma this week, and back or forward to recovery. Self Help with support and useful tools.

Also my involvement with the Corby Safe Haven Crisis House. I am chair of this committee that run this place, a group of service users who employ the manager, deputy manager and staff, and try to keep the Safe Haven open four nights week, again with clients being encouraged to use Mary Ellen's wonderful help books and work sheets and WRAP plans. The staff embrace WRAP and in the Crisis house are a number of TOOLS that the clients can access whilst visiting, such as art and craft supplies, warm, quiet rooms with water features, relaxing music and lamps, a person to talk to, a place to be safe and alone. 🪶

9

Devon, England

Having completed my WRAP course 12 months ago, I have changed considerably. Instead of everyone using me as a doormat like I have been used to letting people do, I won't stand for it anymore. I am constantly battling with people trying to belittle me or putting me down. I have become very aware that I am responsible only for myself and not for others and the way that they choose to operate their own lives. After leaving my 34-year marriage I have become much stronger in myself, dealing with problems as they arise.

I analyze the situation first before I make my conclusion. But I still find it very difficult sometimes to accept the behavior of some of the people around me, even though they know and are fully aware of my past health problems. They still tend to see how far they can push me, to the point that I react rather strongly or simply tell them they they are not any good for me. I need to clear these JEKYLL and HYDE characters completely out of my way in order to pursue my life.

I am completely free of medication now after about 25 years. I can't believe it is true, seeing the professionals stressed at one stage that I would probably be on tablets for the rest of my life.

I have managed since May without tablets and hope I can continue to thrive without them. My sleep pattern is great, I function better through the day and seem to achieve things with very little effort. It's a wonderful feeling after such a long time.

I am far more cautious about everything. I value my health far more than I ever have, without good health you are at a complete loss. Now I have good health I want it to last forever so I can enjoy my life to the full. I am so much happier and enjoy my new lifestyle, without having to be accountable for other people and their garbage!

WORK, REST AND PLAY. I KNOW WHAT LIFE IS ALL
ABOUT AT LAST!!!! ࣾ

10

New Zealand

When I received the email from Mary Ellen asking for personal WRAP stories, I thought, great! Yes, I would like to contribute to this. However, as I sat and pondered how I would structure such a story, I was left with decisions as to where the story should begin. What in my life would be relevant to share with others, so that they could understand why WRAP is important to me and my health? So in the end I decided to do a quick synopsis of my life.

At the age of eighteen months I was severely electrocuted and barely survived with my life. The doctors had told my mother that there may be repercussions later in life for me, but never elaborated on that. So the first six years saw me spend large amounts of time in hospital having reconstructive surgery on my hands.

At the age of two and a half my father died from a brain tumor. My mother was told that it would be unwise to take we children to the funeral, as it would only upset us. They also counseled that it would be easier if she didn't talk about our father either. As you can see my life was full of abandonment issues from the constant hospitalizations, which continued till I was twelve, and the loss of my father.

What nobody understood was the effects of the brain damage from the electrocution, including myself. I grew up feeling very isolated and alone, an onlooker on life, not understanding why I felt so different from others. This continued through my school years and a suicide attempt at eleven. My mother and stepfather thought it best just to be quiet about the attempted overdose. So at a young age, when I may have had some help, it wasn't forthcoming.

I left school and home at fourteen and started work and caring for myself. This continued till I was sixteen when a third suicide attempt had me placed in a large asylum in the mid-seventies. I was never told why I was there. I was never given any information or follow-up after I left. I did, however, know that I would not want to return. In this way I continued to slip through the net of mental health services for the next twenty years.

Major depressive episodes followed me through a bad marriage, and a good career I eventually had to leave through my illness. It was in my early thirties I attended university to gain some paper qualifications for my experience. In the second half of the second year I again crashed. This time, however, so badly that I was taken to see a doctor. He told me I was depressed and asked me to visit a psychiatrist.

This is where my life finally started. At last I knew why I had these feelings. That I had been depressed my whole life without knowing or anyone realizing. My psychiatrist explained to me how the severe electrocution had caused brain damage, had effected the "mood controllers" (his words) in my mind. He started me on medication, promising I would soon be well again. However, I was not medication tolerant, and I spent years trying different pills to no avail. It was during this time I had my first manic high that was recognized as such. Interestingly enough, I was the one who finally realized it was rapid cycling bi polar.

During my thirties I had become increasingly aware that I had issues relating to my childhood. I spent time attending counseling, learning how to live with these issues in the present. I learnt many things about myself and why I reacted in certain ways. I began to monitor my sleep, watch my mood levels etc. Finally, after a long period of not being able to work, I began voluntary work in a service user drop in centre. As I was better able to control my moods and reduce the amount of time I spent in hospital, I began to see that a full life was indeed possible for me again. I joined a peer support group to learn all that I could about the illness and its effects, and most importantly how to keep well. It was at this time I first met Mary Ellen at a conference we held in New Zealand.

Immediately I saw that many of the things I had learnt piecemeal (and those I hadn't) were all neatly laid in a simple structure. I did my WRAP, I followed the principles, I took the facilitator training in the

United States with Mary Ellen. Over the few years since I first met Mary Ellen, WRAP has changed my life dramatically. Yes, I am still medication intolerant, though I do take a small dose of antidepressant. But for all that, I have not had a hospital admission for over four years now. I no longer have a community psychiatric nurse, I manage my illness with the help of my Doctor, who writes a prescription every three months, and my family and friends.

I am now in a stable, happy relationship with a woman I love dearly. I work full time as an advisor for mental health services in our region and am able to do this with minimum time off. Mental health services here now work from a WRAP focus. What more could I ask. Has WRAP helped me? Yes! Yes! Yes! As I explain when I teach WRAP to others, we all have the ability to master our own illness. All we need is the determination to do it. Feel the fear and do it anyway! ❧

11

I never thought I would feel this great and be free of my lifelong pain. It just happened, I was not trying or expecting it to be this way. *How nice it is!* On my journey through life, hard work and struggling, always taking the harder road. I would not do that now. I have learned so much.

In January 1984 and March of the same year, I was in a psychiatric institution just briefly, the first time there from an intensive care unit. On leaving the institution, the only help I had was from a health visitor. The second time was a breakdown from the first and this time I came out on heavier medication.

In 1989, following a breakdown of worrying about someone opening the sluice gates and letting 25, 000 gallons of slurry down the valley, I was in a psychiatric special care unit and then a psychiatric ward. This time I was there much longer. On leaving hospital I had a Community Psychiatric Nurse (CPN) for six months. Then I was discharged from his help, though he remained in the background.

In September 1992, I developed an illness. I worked half load till January 1993, when I was diagnosed with Post Viral Fatigue Syndrome.

I had never heard of this illness, so I kept reading books about the illness, little by little, because my concentration was poor. I could not read much at a time. Seeing it written in black and white about how I was feeling helped me a lot, it was my first step. No one understood how it felt for me, I was isolated *big time*!

The CPN that had previously helped me offered to help. He helped me for six and a half years, Autumn 1992 – Summer 1999, seeing me two times a week at the beginning. I was burned out, sleeping twenty hours a day, having one good day in eight. My doctor was supportive. I'm registered with a different doctor now. He is also very supportive. My CPN classed me as the most highly sensitive person he had worked with in his twenty-five years of nursing. Even putting a piece of Sellotape on a parcel crooked, would give me a pain for up to a week. Another CPN helped me from the Summer 1999 – Summer 2001. When he retired, he wanted me to have a place to go where I could get support. He referred me to a drop-in centre where I was supported by one project worker for six months, another for a year, then the first one again for three years until his leaving.

I finished having one to one support at the end of October 2005, after sixteen years. I now go to a psychotherapy group weekly. I'm standing on my own two feet for the first time. I have always had to lean on someone my whole life. I now know how to turn to my inner self for the support I need. *Life is great!* I'm the happiest I have ever been. I do voluntary work which I enjoy.

My illness path in stages:

1. One good day in eight, for about two years, sometimes sleeping twenty hours a day.

2. Sleeping afternoon for three years, getting up the morning till 11:30ish then sleeping afternoons and getting up for the evening.

3. Wider degrees of remission, going up to three months, with relapses at intervals lasting one to two weeks. As the relapses got shorter, so they were more acute. I have injections of B12 which

helped me with the suicidal effects.

4. Sleeping twelve/fourteen to sixteen hours at night but doing more by day, with quite a short day as I could easily have been in bed by 4:30ish.

5. Much more normal now, just "blips" from time to time, I am much stronger.

6. There are still things I can't do, I lived in silence for nine years, I still don't watch television, I have listened to the radio in the last four years. The sound on earlier was too much. The television did, and still does, put me too much in touch with the problems I have had in my own life, which did become extra baggage to carry. So to me it seemed pointless to watch television as I was soaking it up like a sponge.

With professional people, to date I felt I always had the best. I still have a care co-coordinator who is one of the best. He said when I was talking about some one traveling abroad that I have already traveled many more miles than he has. When I went to the drop-in centre I learnt how to develop my mind and how to interact with people again. Making proper conversation rather than just talking about myself, my pain and my distress. In the early stages I did jigsaw puzzles there to get myself focused. The project workers helped me by doing activities with me to help my mind. They play scrabble, upwards and snooker.

I was greatly helped by the WRAP plan, even though there were parts of me doing this before I knew of it. Like listening to my doctor saying, "Only go with the flow, listen to your body and only do in a day things you want to do". Meaning that this would heal me, rather than go against the grain, which would just make me ill. The main parts of the WRAP plan I found useful were the triggers and listening to them. Also knowing not to have to put up with toxic friends! Just walk away before they make you ill. I got a lot out of delivering the WRAP plan to groups of people with a facilitator. I got training days run by mental health involvement workers, which has built up my confidence. ❧

12

Republic of Ireland

I have suffered from schizophrenia and subsequently, manic depression, since the age of 19 years. Looking back over the years, I was lucky to survive and to live to tell the story today.

My depression manifested itself when I went to university at the age of 18 and whilst recovering somewhat from the depression, it was still haunting me in the background. I would spend periods in bed, not doing the basics, such as washing or looking after my clothes, eating properly, not holding down a job for very long periods of time. At the age of 30 this depression got worse.

I was very happy when my children were born and loved them dearly but I found as I went on I wasn't able to look after them. I was also in a very unhappy marriage and prior to that my first partner (the children's father) died suddenly at the age of 44. Events became a bit drastic when I tried to commit suicide on a number of occasions, but, Thank God, I survived.

After my last visit to the psychiatric hospital (which was 4 years ago), I knew it was now or never. My children had been fostered for a number of years. I loved them dearly, had good access to them but always longed to have them home. A senior psychiatric social worker introduced me to the WRAP program 4 years ago and I can honestly say, by going through the very basic and daily steps for daily maintenance and recovery, it has meant so much to me. As I say, it was now or never. We talked and she read out the program to me, discussed it with me and gave me little exercises to do. She explained the importance of each step and I took it from there.

Thankfully I am leading a very happy life now. I carry out my daily maintenance tasks every day (whether I feel up to it or not). I attend a day centre for support. I work 3 days a week in a pretty stressful job and most importantly of all, my son has come home to live with me full time. My daughter comes to me most weekends. She is having a wonderful time with her foster parents and goes abroad regularly. I live with my son and stepson. Thankfully things have brightened up for me.

I know it is by working on the WRAP program that I have really come a long way. My determination is to keep going and maintain myself, my son and my daughter to the best of my ability. I have learned that I mustn't give up or give in. I have learned to believe in myself. Keep doing my daily tasks and have friends to phone or talk with. The Samaritans are very good, but for me, having a family friend is worth millions. ☙

Using Wellness Tools

Developing the Wellness Toolbox was an eye-opening experience for me. I had never considered the vast store of resources that are easily accessible to me that I could use to help myself feel better in difficult times and to enhance my life in general. Even though I had come a long way in my own recovery, as I worked on this list I began to feel more power and sense of control over my life.

That list has become very important to me. I have added to it over the years as I learn and try new things. It is now very long and takes up many pages at the beginning of my WRAP binder. I use it whenever I upgrade my WRAP to more closely meet my current needs and lifestyle. In addition, whenever I feel like it, I check out that list and come up with some great things to do to enhance my life. I may not even open the book, I can just think of that list and come up with great things to do. For a while, when it was shorter, I had this list hanging on the front of my refrigerator for easy access.

In WRAP workshops and in the correspondence I receive from people, many of them say the Wellness Toolbox is the most important part of their plan. It was when learning about Wellness Tools that they first began to realize that they could do things to help themselves. Some even said this part of the plan is so significant that they have never bothered to develop the rest of the plan. They refer to that list whenever they need to.

In this chapter, I want to share some stories that specifically speak to the Wellness Toolbox and specific Wellness Tools.

1

I have been battling depression for as long as I can remember. Because my guardians were from the era when mental health issues were taboo, I went undiagnosed for several years, in spite of showing every sign of depression.

I became a workaholic, thinking that was what I was supposed to do. I even tried to do the geographical change by moving. Little did I know I was running away from all my problems. After a four-year relationship break-up, I hit a bottom. I saw the ghosts from the past coming from the front door of my apartment. I decided that there and then, things would come to an end. I did not want to pass this down to my children, should I have any. I went to counseling in August of 1994. I was hospitalized in November and December of the same year. I have multiple diagnoses.

To be honest, I have not been in WRAP that long. When I started WRAP, we went over the "tool box." That was the first day I learned my life could be more manageable. That was when I learned things in my life could be "fixed." I could relate to it as I am a nontraditional female. I like to fix cars, plumbing and such. You should see my toolbox!

I am looking forward to what WRAP has to offer. So far, I have found it very educational. I believe it is helpful as it offers hope. It may take work on my part, but I am willing to do it. I am ever so grateful WRAP is there to help me with my life.

My Wellness Tool Box consists of a variety of things, just like my toolboxes at home. One thing is my DBT (Dialectical Behavioral Therapy) skills. Even though I need to use my DBT skills on a daily basis, sometimes, when I get down, I need a reminder to use my skills. I also have what I call, "Lutherizing," which is listening to a Luther Van Dross CD or watching one of his DVD(s). After I "Lutherize," I am calm and it is like a brand new day. It is the same way as "Anitaizing," which is listening to a specific Anita Baker CD.

I have a picture of my Dad. He died when I was four. I have fond memories of him. The picture is there not only to remind me of the comfort he gave me, but to let me know he wouldn't want me to be in misery during the times I am down.

Then I have my actual toolbox. It reminds me of how I like to fix and to make things. This reminder makes me proud of the accomplishments I have made, such as putting down a linoleum tile floor for the first time ever and having it turn out well, in spite of having to trash a pair of jeans because of the tile glue getting on them.

I have a telephone to remind me to pick up the phone and call my friends. If things are severe enough, I can call the YWCA hotline, my therapist or doctor, as they are on call 24/7.

There are photos of some pictures I have drawn or painted. I either get prompted to draw or create something, or I feel proud of the ones I have done.

Just like any toolbox, more tools will be added throughout time. In my case, it will be to the point of where I'll need another toolbox. I am expecting this to be true of my Wellness Tool Box. 🐦

2

The Power of WRAP

The other day I had a very direct experience of the 'Power of WRAP'. I was ushering at a show at the local theater called "Laughing Wild" by Christopher Durang. I had heard that the play had three acts: 1) Woman 2) Man, 3) Man and Woman. Act 1-Woman was a monologue that put psychiatric illness in a theatrically 'humorous' light. It was totally insulting. The character was flip, silly, annoying, crude and portrayed as the very typical wacky ex-Creedmore patient that non-survivors love to laugh at. I left the play after the first act. I just could not face sweetly selling cookies and refreshments to audience members after viewing this character, and had no wish to see how the play ended.

To put it in WRAP terms, I felt "triggered". I wrote in my journal, pondering about the theaters' portrayal of insanity in general. I was wondering if, once upon a time, I too would have laughed at the wackiness of the monologue. The sense that the playwright had gotten inside of the character's mind, the woman as "nut" mind, and expressed it so enter-tainingly: the jokes, pauses, imagined exchanges, so easy to laugh at for those who have never actually experienced mental illness.

The trigger for me in this situation was really the loneliness of not laughing along. The insecurity that somehow, through his creative ge-nius, Christopher Durang knew the workings of the mind of the ex-patient better than myself. That somehow his character was more real than the many survivors and in-patients that I have met through my work with WRAP. Suddenly there was this huge wall between myself and the other people in the audience. This is a very successful comedy in the theater world. I wanted to run onstage, tell her to stop entertain-ing the world with her stories. But maybe it was especially triggering because deep down I sensed that so many want their stories expressed as convincingly as Durang's character, yet never get that chance. The energy of the exchange between the performer and audience is so powerful and cathartic. Everyone is brought to a new level of perception.

And maybe there are some in the audience who will someday face mental health challenges themselves. They may be haunted by the stigma created by a 'comedy' show such as "Laughing Wild". Or did I miss the whole point? Are we as a society supposed to laugh at the ex-patient and her behavior? Are we all better off if we can find humor in the darkest, and sometimes, most humiliating moments?

The experience created a lot of confusion and profound questions. My experience as a WRAP facilitator helped support me. I felt connect-ed at a deeper level to a community that seeks to heal itself of past psy-chiatric trauma. My journaling helped me see the bigger picture. I also felt stronger in warding off the stigma that viewing the play created. This character does not speak for all of us. Nobody does, really. The WRAP, though a formula, does not pigeonhole individuals into diagnoses. The character in Durang's play was struggling with this through her goofball monologue. I still have respect for the play as an art form. It's about how the audience responds at a gut level. I was free to walk away and deal with my own issues. The WRAP helped me through the turmoil. ð𝕪

3
From Ink And Paper To Everyday Life

Sometimes it's hard for me to put into words how I took my WRAP training from ink and paper to actually applying it to my everyday life. The first time I actually used my WRAP training was in a real life crisis and it saved me. I used it to help myself and save myself. WRAP gave me empowerment over serious psychiatric crisis.

It was 8:00 pm on a Friday night and I just crashed emotionally, mentally, and physically. It was so bad I didn't want to live. Life is not supposed to be like this. I was alone. I was scared; I didn't know what to do. I'd just moved into this beautiful new apartment. I wasn't homeless anymore, but I was so alone. I remembered not wanting to live like this anymore. I was being swallowed up in this pit of doom. I needed help. I looked up at the picture of my children and all I could think was "call someone". I couldn't think straight. There was no cocaine, no alcohol, no pills; none of my normal vices to take away the pain. CALL SOME-ONE.

I called the suicide hotline and was promptly put on hold. When the young lady came back on the line, one of the first things she asked me was, did I feel like harming myself? My answer was YES, I WANT TO DIE. She was a nice young lady, but she was not able to help me, and asked that I leave my number and someone would call me back within the next 30 minutes or so. I told her "Honey, I'll be dead by then," and all she could do was ask for my phone number again. I left my number and hung up the phone.

My situation just went from bad to worse. I was going through my book bag looking for my phone book and I pulled out my WRAP folder. When I opened it the first thing I saw was my Certificate of Achievement for completing the workshop. It gave me a good feeling. I started to read. The first thing I read was Focusing- "How does it feel inside my body right now? What's between me and feeling fine?" I continued to read for the next hour. I read this book from cover to cover until 2:00 am.

I was calm. I took control. The Suicide Hotline did call back maybe an hour later. At that point it was just an interruption in my focusing. I spoke with her long enough to reassure her that I wasn't thinking about hurting myself anymore.

I was able to go back over the last several days and I knew then what the triggers were, what the early warning sign were. I made a list of these things to watch for. My WRAP folder is with me just about wherever I go. I've put together my support system. I have more than one number to call should this happen again. I've gained so much strength from this training. The facilitator of the WRAP training has been a Godsend to me, along with my other supporters, who have had the training, too. I will use WRAP for the rest of my life. I share my training and my folder, with just about everyone. I have almost completed my Advance Directive. It's like having additional life insurance. My wishes will be respected and followed. WRAP is a part of my everyday life. I'm thankful that this has brought this into my life. It's wonderful to work through what life can throw you, without turning to drugs and alcohol, and to begin to take charge of how I want to live. ৵

4

On June 13, 2005, at 10:00 am I began my WRAP Training. I was given pen, paper and highlighter in various colors, and a lime green folder, which contained pertinent information about my WRAP data. And a slide projector was in view to give me images of what I was about to learn. With these tools in hand I was ready to begin my wellness journey. We took several breaks, but the BIG BREAK came when I applied my WRAP training in my everyday life.

I'll tell you several incidents where WRAP saved my life. It all started when I was awakened early one morning with my left hand in excruciating pain. My hand was swollen and I couldn't use it. This particular pain was worse than labor pain. I knew something was wrong so I took a cab to the hospital. Once I arrived in emergency, I was asked a series of questions. Then I was taken in a room to wait for a doctor. While waiting the pain became unbearable and I started screaming and shouting to the top of my voice. Finally the doctor came in and pointed his finger in my face and told me to be quiet in a mean way and that other people were before me. Then he left.

I began to calm down and take some deep breaths and not allow myself to become angry and do something crazy. I knew I had worked my WRAP that morning because without it I could have been in jail. When the doctor came back in he had a different attitude. He told me my hand would be X-rayed and once the results were back he would tell me what was going on. I found out I had sprung my hand and a splint would be put on it. I was also given a prescription for the pain that made me sick and didn't work.

I decided a few days later to go to my doctor and he looked at my hand and put me on some heavy narcotics. The label said, "may cause drowsiness". At first I didn't care because of the pain and I just wanted it to go away. I didn't consider that I was a recovering addict and that this could be the start of an addiction all over again. Even through it wasn't crack it was a substitute. I had been told by a couple of people I shouldn't take this but I wanted to anyway. All I could think of was "pain, pain, go away". Well, to make a long story short, I did get the prescription, but once I got home and had it in my hand, I felt something come over me and said, "You don't need that, I forbid you to take it. You've come too far in 2 and a half years."

As tears flowed down my eyes I know there was a Guardian Angel watching over me. But the joy of it all is because I changed my negative thoughts into positive ones. *Because I used my WRAP I didn't use the drug*. And guess what? The pain went away and I found closure in this case and my goal was achieved. Thank you WRAP. 🕊

5
Peer Support Helped Bring Family Back Together

I remember looking up at a beautiful blue sky, and feeling the brisk cold breeze on my face, and thinking about how hurting my heart was, as I headed into a friend's office. I was so hurt. My youngest son whom I adore wanted nothing to do with me. I couldn't really blame him. After all, I'd been addicted to drugs all of his life and spent more time in jail than I did at his side, so why shouldn't he be angry? He didn't ask to be born, and certainly not to a drug addicted parent! He'd given me countless opportunities to be in his life and I'd blown each and every one of them. What was I supposed to do? How can I make him see that I'm serious? "You can't", my friend said. "You can't force your way into his life. There's not going to be a parade in your honor because you've finally decided to live your life clean. You're on his time now. You're going to have to earn his trust." She spoke of her daughter and how she too had longed to have her in her life but had to be patient. She told me of how she would send short "thinking of you" notes with no expectations or demands. I tried it. I prayed. I waited and then I left it with God.

One day, while sitting at home reading a delicious book, my doorbell buzzed. I picked up the phone to find my son at the other end. My heart was racing as I thought WHAT'S THE PROBLEM… "Mama," he said. "It's me and I just stopped to check on you." I could feel the warm tears running down my cheeks, just as they are now, as I whispered, "Thank you" to the Heavens above. Since then I've been invited to dinner, to his home and spend week ends with my grandson.

Thank you WRAP for giving me the tools in my Wellness box that enabled me and my son to come back together as a family. ❧

6

I am the coordinator of a Peer Support Center. My center has been in the WRAP program for one year now. Speaking for myself, I have found the program to be very helpful in my recovery.

I did a power point presentation on WRAP for my center. All of us are supposed to be raised right, I just forgot after I got grown. I made " Never forget how I was raised" Number 1 on Developing a Wellness Tool Box. This made me a better person and helped my professional and private life. ટ≫

7
Living Well With a Bipolar II Mood Disorder

My symptoms recurred over 28 years: on-again off-again episodes of depression with anxiety, dark thoughts and blue moods, interspersed with high-energy phases and irritable outbursts. Periodically, I consulted physicians, psychologists and psychiatrists. As a trusting and a cooperative patient, I tried pills and therapy but was dismissed, misdiagnosed, mistreated, lied to and laughed at. At age 45, I was finally diagnosed with a bipolar II mood disorder, a form of manic depression. For the first time, I had the right medical words to understand myself. I wasn't mad, sad or bad, just a person with a mood disorder.

Desperate for help, I updated my Bachelor of Science degree (in biological and medical sciences and psychology) by studying self-help books, psychiatry texts and psychology references. Alone with my symptoms, I needed the reassurance that comes from learning how other people cope with mental problems. Even though I was not well, *The Depression Workbook: A Guide for Living With Depression and Manic Depression* by Mary Ellen Copeland inspired me to learn and renewed my hope for recovery. Reading became my first wellness recovery tool.

Eventually I read the practice guidelines of psychiatry. They recommend accurate diagnosis and effective treatments. Would any competent psychiatrist short cut the guidelines by just labeling a sick patient without diagnostic tests? Why rush to prescribe pills like antidepressants, tranquilizers, anticonvulsants and mood stabilizers? Lithium for bipolars, SSRIs for depressives. Sounds quick and easy but what if the medications make a sick patient worse? What if a misdiagnosis leads to a wrong prescription? For months as my pills made me worse, I thought about suicide – I just wanted the pain to end. As my doctor increased the doses, I deteriorated. I desperately wanted to recover.

Nobody likes it when a moody patient gets sicker, not the doctor, not the family and certainly not the patient. The system has three labels for the worst cases – refractory depression, treatment resistance and borderline personality. My psychiatrist, a published expert specializing in mood disorders, wrote 'The Clinical Meaning of Refractory Depression' for the *American Journal of Psychiatry* in which he defined "refractory depression" as problems with diagnosis and problems with treatment. That brainy expert repeatedly noted "refractory depression" in my medical file and kept writing prescriptions. He did not revisit my diagnosis or revise my treatment plan. While I deteriorated, he shortcut 13 standard procedures. For months, he increased doses and smiled as his pills caused side attacks and toxic effects.

The stigma of a chronic mental illness distances depressives from healthy friends and family. Fault finding and excluding do not help when sick people need medical care, encouragement and support. Instinctively, I sought other people with similar problems, hoping to learn how they got well. Networking became my second wellness recovery tool. At mood disorder association meetings, I met people with diagnoses like depression, manic depression and dysthymia. Most of them were anxious and unsettled, wondering about their symptoms, treatments and prognosis. I felt comfortable with my moody tribe, welcomed and understood. While discussing our problems, we monitored our progress. We compared symptoms, side effects, diagnoses and therapies. Some people did well on high doses of meds, while others, like me, could not tolerate even low doses of our brain pills. Some talk therapies helped us improve our patterns of thinking, feeling and behaving, but it was hard to make progress when we were sick.

I started an independent depression project and interviewed more than 150 depressed people and family members, while studying the mental healthcare system and researching books and articles. One woman suggested the *Journal of Orthomolecular Medicine*. Imagine my surprise to find helpful information about restorative care just two miles from home in Toronto. The friendly editor of the *Journal of Medicine* offered the booklist, newsletter, and annual conference. Still cranky after years of bad moods and failed treatments, I could not resist this pleasant invitation to read about restorative care. My curiosity was aroused by the scientific and medical research, the fifty-year history and success of orthomolecular medicine and the progress reports of recovered patients. Would ortho-care heal my brain?

Skeptical, I tried a third wellness recovery tool–orthomolecular medicine. Disillusioned after years of failed doctor-patient relationships and determined to avoid shortcuts, I read about health professionals who apply the life science of biochemistry to the art of medicine. Thanks to a little yellow book, *The Way Up From Down*, by California psychiatrist Dr. Priscilla Slagle, whose own mood disorder resolved when she tried orthomolecular medicine, I learned how to take nutritional supplements. I had already responded quickly to an extract of the world's oldest plant, *Gingko biloba*, but some symptoms continued. A basic orthomolecular regimen of vitamins, minerals and amino acids, taken one-by-one and continued if they helped, soon restored my mental health.

At conferences in Toronto and Vancouver I met recovered patients and interviewed orthomolecular doctors. I read many books about orthomolecular medicine, and was intrigued by the work of Dr. Abram Hoffer, whose more than 30 books include *Adventures in Psychiatry: The Scientific Memoirs of Dr. Abram Hoffer*. He and his colleague, Dr. Humphrey Osmond, co-founded orthomolecular medicine in Canada in the 1950s while researching schizophrenia, developing an adrenochrome theory and customizing restorative regimens for psychotic patients. Their regimen for schizophrenia did not work for me; my diagnosis of bipolar disorder meant that I needed a different regimen. *Nutrition & Mental Illness* by Dr. Carl Pfeiffer, another colleague of Dr. Hoffer's, explained how one of three regimens could help, depending on each patient's diagnosis and biochemical individuality. Dr. Pfeiffer's histamine-lowering regimen worked best for me.

The orthomolecular concept makes sense. A depressed brain needs to refuel its energy, stabilize its enzymes, balance its neurotransmitters and restore its capabilities. As a sick brain heals, symptoms resolve. The restored brain no longer misfires; bad moods pass; life looks brighter. A bipolar brain also needs to control its tendency to get overexcited. Fortunately, GABA, the brain's inhibitory neurotransmitter, taken as a supplement, calmed me right away. I added TMG (trimethylglycine) and l-taurine and the trace minerals magnesium, zinc and manganese. They worked! With Dr. Slagle's book as a professional guide, I slowly tested the B vitamins 1, 2, 5, 6 and 12, vitamin D and the antioxidant vitamins C and E. Guided by other books and two doctors, I am taking mitochondrial supplements l-carnitine with ribose and co-enzyme Q-10 and the trace minerals chromium and selenium.

At age 50, new symptoms started – problems with memory, focus and sleeping, low energy and low libido. After reading a newspaper article about a male hormone deficiency, I found a family doctor who would prescribe testosterone supplements. That helped right away. I got a second opinion from Dr. Jerald Bain, a Toronto endocrinologist and medical professor who specializes in andropause and edited *Mechanisms in Andropause*. Under his care, I continued my bipolar regimen and adjusted the supplements of testosterone, which also works restoratively.

Since 1996, an orthomolecular regimen of vitamins, minerals, amino acids, energy and enzyme co-factors, essential fatty acids, hormones and antioxidants has complemented my antidepressant-anxiolytic medication (an extract of *Gingko biloba*). I have been stable for ten years, with no more episodes of depression or hypomania. After years of painful problems, black and blue moods and symptoms of a bipolar II mood disorder, migraines and anxiety, restorative care helped me recover and stay well.

Volunteering became my fourth wellness recovery tool. As an independent volunteer, I can help myself keep well while helping the International Society of Orthomolecular Medicine with their Open Minds campaign—orthomolecular public education and networking. Ten years ago, I started writing books and articles and telling people about restorative care. I appeared in the documentary film *Masks of Madness: Science of Healing* and spoke at four conferences on Nutritional Medicine Today. When people ask about my books or web site, www.searpubl.ca, I introduce them to restorative orthomolecular care.

I worked hard to develop a Wellness Recovery Action Plan which has four key tools: (1) bibliotherapy (reading books by recovered patients and health professionals), (2) networking (with support organizations, patients, caregivers and physicians), (3) taking a daily orthomolecular regimen and (4) volunteering. My bipolar brain is not perfect, but good enough to work, get along with family and friends, consult with clients, write, network and tell people about orthomolecular medicine: restorative treatments for beautiful minds. Even when things get tough, my WRAP tools help me find competent health professionals, ask for quality medical care, avoid relapse and live well with a mood disorder. 🐾

8
Action Plans to the Rescue!

I recently found out by e-mail that one of my favorite friends has cancer. Since I couldn't talk to her, I didn't know any more specific information. Sometimes news like that sends me into a real tizzy, but I consciously decided to take a WRAP approach and try some new action plan ideas. First I sent her some flowers at work with a card that said, "From one of your team members". When she called to thank me, I found out she has cancer in her eye area. She has to have two surgeries. As other action plans, I decided to reach out to three other friends of mine who also have cancer.

One has been having chemotherapy and radiation and has not been out very much for a long time, so I invited her for lunch the next day. We had a wonderful 3-hour girlfriend lunch.

The second had recently come home from the clinic and has been unable to comfortably write or read so she has been watching a lot of TV. I called her and asked if she would be interested in some books on CD. She was really happy with the idea, so I went to the library and got her a varied assortment and took them over to her.

Then I called my friend, the third friend, who lives in Florida, and we talked about my coming down to see her this Fall, which made us both happy. We haven't seen each other in a long time and she is one of my dearest and most special friends.

I didn't tell these friends about April or about each other. All day long I felt my power coming back, and by the late afternoon I was feeling good. I was eating dinner at a restaurant with my husband and my dad, when I was surprised to see my friend with cancer walking in the door. By that time, I was able to greet her with a happy and reassuring demeanor because I had been working action plans all day.

Later that week, she called and invited me to meet her for dinner. She trusted me enough to talk to me about her concerns about her situation. I don't think she would have wanted to talk to me if I had been upset and negative when she saw me right after I got the news. My action plans helped me be the kind of friend I wanted to be for her. They also helped me be a good friend to myself! ❧

9

You might be interested in a little story about me. Last September I realized that I had been slowing sliding into a really major depression for more than a year. After all my years of using and adapting my WRAP and teaching about Early Warning Signs and When Things are Breaking Down, I had missed my own. I was shocked. I hadn't recognized it because it was so gradual. It came in a different way, because I expected "it" would never happen again, and on some level I felt ashamed and that I was just "lazy" or that what I was feeling was somehow not valid.

After a major triggering experience this fall, which I *did* recognize, I gradually became aware of what was going on. I was shocked that I had gone so long without recognizing it. But it was a major relief to recognize it and to be able to put words around it and meet it face-to-face.

I have redone my WRAP, of course, and in a way that I think will prevent this long-term thing from ever happening again (new tools, among them: drumming, which is so healing; better monitoring; better use of my support system). I also have a better sense of how to work with people to revise WRAPs, since I know when it's needed, etc. I will be doing a section about that in our upcoming workshop. ❧

10

One idea I have is a 'personal area.' A place one goes to daily, such as a mirror, with personal objects, watch, comb, etc. The placing of mental health material there would remind and motivate the consumer to 'awake and carry on.' I guess it is maybe some subliminal thought coming from Mother Russia's 'Red Corner.' ❧

WRAP Stories from WRAP Facilitators

Now we move on to WRAP Stories from the perspective of people who have been trained as WRAP facilitators and lead WRAP groups.

I want to introduce you to stories by people who are WRAP facilitators so you can see what WRAP and facilitating WRAP groups means to them. I think you will be amazed at the variety and complexity of circumstances that brought them to the place in their lives where they wanted to share WRAP with others. As you will see, many of them have their own story of mental health difficulties and years of despair before finding wellness, recovery and fulfillment by leading WRAP groups. Others come from a more professional background.

1

WRAP has been an integral part of my life since 1998. I have been able to lead two WRAP groups a week for 8 years. This experience has allowed me to talk and think with other consumers each week about WRAP and how I use my days and minutes to recover and keep healthy, both mentally and physically.

Many of the consumers in my groups had abusive childhoods, poverty issues, lacked social skills, suffered from isolation, lacked education due to their mental disabilities, had eating disorders due to medications, many serious diseases due to side effects of medications, and did not have financial resources to enable them to get needed help.

Each member of my groups during these 8 years received what they were ready to receive from WRAP. Some just got the crisis assistance they needed. Some really got the WRAP approach and have not been hospitalized since.

Only two consumers were hospitalized in my 8 years leading WRAP groups. Every person who came to my group received fellowship and individual attention with their issues of recovering. They were not alone in the world anymore. They all received a weekly phone call, and for some that was the support and fellowship they needed to get moving forward.

The second thing that everyone got in our groups was ideas. New options for how they could do their daily life, crisis, etc. One woman who has come to the group often has learned very slowly to exercise, walk, and join in something fun, a sewing class. Another man has felt the strength to see himself as a co-leader of the group, and learned to teach instead of sit and isolate himself when in a group. The socialization skills learned by group members were incredible. Many consumers learned to talk as well as listen, as the group was a safe place; and through helping others in the group, were able to see their own lives as recovering, and improve their daily choices.

Many consumers started new activities. Lots of consumers started taking courses at the local community college, or volunteering in the community center, or working part-time. Often, they came back for help when it all didn't go well. However, many for the first time had the experience of a successful class, or job. Some consumers are still involved in those activities. I served over 100 consumers in the last two years.

For myself, as a WRAP group facilitator and peer counselor, I was privileged to sit and think with others of my days and hours and minutes and how I choose to spend each minute. The most important event in WRAP for me has been, through the groups, to decide to be recovered. Recovery is a choice and an intention, and I truly got the opportunity to practice each minute of every day the recovery, WRAP, and fellowship with other consumers. In each group I had the opportunity to re-connect with my intention to RECOVER. I also learned that Recovery and WRAP has to do with connecting with ourselves, and completely engaging with what I am doing. Often, I had been passive, and just followed the day. In my WRAP, I took charge of my day, and crisis, and early warning signs. I became aware of the signs of crisis before they became a big crisis. I avoid crisis today, and enjoy a life where I am in charge of my days.

I also learned how to monitor myself, and be aware of my physical and emotional stuff while it is going on, kind of an inner awareness that has developed through WRAP and recovery ideas. The biggest deal in WRAP for me has been the daily plan and the toolbox that helps me to do the activities that keep me healthy. After 6 years or so of using a daily plan, I now have a flexible plan using different tools depending on my current physical and emotional stuff. I am monitoring myself.

In the last 8 years, the biggest problem I have had is from the side effects of psychiatric medications and also the times when a specific medication no longer works.

It has been wonderful to share with my WRAP groups my frustrations with these medications. However, in sharing my problems and frustrations, I clearly learned a whole lot of information from consumers about various medications, and this was incredibly valuable in my search to keep healthy.

Obviously, I am incredibly grateful for the WRAP information, and the role it has played in my life through the use of WRAP group facilitation and peer counseling.

I am in awe of the use of the plan with consumers in group settings where everyone "gets to win" and be recovered. There were no failures in our WRAP groups. ❧

2
Wrap Story

The mail had arrived that morning many years ago and the questionnaire I'd been expecting was finally there. I'd responded to an inquiry seeking individuals with a bi-polar diagnosis to complete a questionnaire from a lady doing a research project. She seemed sincere and I was glad to be of help.

I can still picture me as I sat at my kitchen table, pondering my responses, crying a few tears as memories resurfaced of my hospitalizations and ECT. It took me a while to complete the questionnaire, as I recalled good and bad times along the path back to feeling like myself again. I shared a bit about the self-help method I'd been using, called Recovery Inc. I wanted to say so much to her but figured I'd just do what was requested. I then mailed it back to Mary Ellen Copeland.

I well remember the first book that Mary Ellen published. I was excited to know my responses had been helpful. She utilized the results from that study to begin the works and writings that she continues to this day. I watched her career and her writings evolve. I felt like we were kindred spirits, although it was a long while before I came to know her personally. I have grown to know and respect her through the years since our first encounter. I was proud to take facilitator training from her.

I facilitated WRAP classes for 6 years as part of the core curriculum in Rochester, New York, at the Family Service of Rochester's Main St. Intensive Psychiatric Rehabilitation Program (IPRT), where I was employed as a psychiatric rehabilitation counselor. The program assisted individuals with a mental health diagnosis to establish a goal and do what was needed to obtain and maintain that goal. Goals were set in one of four environments: vocational, educational, social or housing. As I had used WRAP personally, I knew its worth and its help to me. I chose to teach the classes in a group setting, with each individual doing their own plan at their own pace. We ordered a WRAP book for each person to use.

Along with WRAP as a core course, people also took Taking Charge. Taking Charge was an introduction to Recovery Inc's mental health self-help method. The method and tools I'd learned and utilized to help myself were shared with the participants in Taking Charge classes. Individuals incorporated those tools into their WRAP plans to assist them in changing their thoughts and commanding their muscles. I watched people flourish as they worked toward and completed their goals. They demonstrated self-help and self-empowerment.

Helping others is important to me. I know that making and using my own WRAP plans are meaningful. My plan includes practice of Recovery's method and participation in weekly meetings. This is the best way I can continue to be self-led and not symptom-led, helping myself to be the best I can be. Recovery Inc. is celebrating its 70th year in 2007. My hope is that more and more individuals will become aware of the dynamic duo, Recovery Inc. weekly meetings and WRAP. ॐ

3

I first learned about WRAP in 2003 while working as a Rehabilitation Specialist. I went through the 3-day training but never utilized the skills I had learned in implementing WRAP. I moved to another area in 2004 and began working again as a Rehabilitation Specialist. I began to implement my knowledge of WRAP and am pleased to say that I have seen a remarkable change in many of the consumers that are coming to the groups. Individuals who would normally not participate in group are raising their hands and sharing information. In others, I have seen a boost of self-esteem. Others are now able to identify their triggers and coping skills. But above all, I have seen a tremendous improvement in their leadership skills. Approximately 20 peers have "graduated" from WRAP and have begun facilitating groups of their own. Groups ranging from mental health to art. Some of the peers have begun to implement the WRAP Peer Support group and are taking active roles in helping other peers understand, complete, and implement their WRAP groups. I praise them daily for the accomplishments and remind them that they too can be a success. As far as my future role in WRAP, I have made it clear to the consumers that as the mental health system in our state progresses, WRAP will no longer be led by staff, but by peer support specialists, and they are anxiously waiting for the moment to arrive. ❧

4

Teaching WRAP

Teaching WRAP is the ultimate form of learning WRAP. A WRAP trainer has to be a model of recovery, so people will start to believe they can recover too. He must understand the concepts well enough to explain them lots of different ways, and to explain why each one is important. He must be able to answer questions he could not possibly anticipate. He must embody a recovery ethic and philosophy so well that it is part of who he is, not just what he teaches. There might be a way of teaching WRAP without living it and feeling it passionately, but I don't know what that way would be. It's a very hands-on, personal kind of teaching.

I've been doing it almost ten years now, most recently with inpatients in a state hospital. The first time I was asked to name five supporters, I could only name my mother and my therapist. And the first time I was told to take personal responsibility for my choices, I replied, "You mean all the terrible things that happened to me are my fault!" (They're not your fault, but when they happen, it's your choice what you do next, and you're responsible for that choice.) And the first time I used my WRAP to beat a depression in a day and a half instead of going to bed for a week or two, just knowing I could do it changed my life. It was the first time I had ever controlled my moods instead of having my moods control me.

People have told me I've changed their lives. It's not true, but it's flattering and nice to hear. What really is true is that these people were sick and tired of being sick and tired. They were looking for a different approach to living with their issues. I came along with a viable approach that I communicated well. It was their choice to try it, and to keep it up when the training was over. They did it, not me and not the program. It was a good message, I was a good messenger, but they changed their own lives.

I had one trainee about five years ago who was often afraid to leave her house. She had terrifying symptoms: when triggered, she would go somewhere for a while, and come back not knowing where she'd been or how long she'd been gone, with no memory of what happened while she was (her word) "altered". Today, she's vice-chair of the state mental health consumer council and a speaker for NAMI's In Our Own Voice speakers bureau, where she tells her recovery story to all kinds of people. She conducts staff orientation at her mental health center, where she also sits on committees that interview job applicants and review consumer complaints. She's appeared in newspaper features, attended national consumer conferences. About three years ago, I told her to stop telling people she was "unemployed." What she does rises to the level of professional consulting in the mental health field, and it's nobody's business where she gets her money.

She gives me credit for all that. I keep correcting her. The important thing for me as her teacher is that I don't believe it myself. She's my personal proof that you don't have to be "high functioning" or well educated to get well.

She's my most dramatic success story, but not my only one. Last summer, I did a presentation on using WRAP to cope with voices. Lots of people came up after that and said it changed their lives. I told Pat Deegan the same thing when I first heard her speak about non-medical coping skills for voices in 1995. What was life-changing for me was that hearing voices is a symptom of an illness only if it interferes with the person you want to be and the way you want to live – if the voices are telling you to kill yourself, or hate yourself, or giving you commands it takes all your energy to resist, or making it too difficult to focus on what's going on around you. If not, find a little time in the day when it's safe to listen to them. If you try to stifle them all the time, they come out in ways and at times that are inconvenient and damaging to you. It takes too much energy to keep them tamped down all the time, and no medicine will make them go away completely. You might learn something from them, like what's in your deepest heart, or which direction your moods and emotions are going. Some cultures (Pat Deegan again) consider voices like that a spiritual gift, and not an illness at all. As for medicine, you have to make a personal calculation – how intrusive and unpleasant are your voices, how much relief does the medicine give you, and is the relief worth the side effects? And finally, can you use coping skills to reduce the amount of medicine you need, even if you can't eliminate medicine completely?

This sounds like common sense, but it wasn't to me until 1995, and it wasn't to these conferees until 2005. Many said it was life changing. And it's a very rare doctor who thinks about coping skills as a viable way to reduce the need for medicine. Some still think you need to take as much as you can stand, instead of as little as you need to have a good life. And some think every inner voice requires a pill. People with spiritual gifts still have to be wary of many psychiatrists.

If you never thought that way before, imagine how liberating a thought it could be. Do I enjoy being that messenger? It almost makes all my years of starving and suffering worth it, just so I can give back in this way.

At the hospital where I teach, we call plans for Daily Maintenance, Triggers and Early Warning Signs "relapse prevention plans". This is not to please hospital management by making WRAP sound medical. It's to make the message immediate and compelling to the trainees. When they are in the hospital, they care about two things: getting out and not coming back. So here's a way of not coming back. We say the same about making your post-crisis plan while you're in the hospital but feeling OK. My treatment providers think I'm Houdini because I'm so good at using my triggers and early warning signs plans. That's how I'm able to teach them with so much enthusiasm and urgency. Often, people will go along with my enthusiasm when they still think the method can't possibly help them because they are beyond help. Later, they come to see themselves as having some control over their moods and difficulties.

I always talk about my first big depression after my first WRAP course. I beat something in a day and a half that, before, would have flattened me for a week or two. I used about nine of the coping skills I'd just learned. I like to tell this story because, as Henry Kissinger used to say, "it has the added advantage of being true." It also ends funny. I flirted with a woman for 30 minutes and the depression was gone – which in WRAP terms is a "diversionary activity."

I've learned that I have to set boundaries. I no longer do one-on-one peer support with my WRAP trainees. They can be very needy, and it can get awkward before you realize it. They see something in you that makes them want to latch on, and that's bad for me and for them. This is especially true now that I'm in a committed relationship. We're lucky in our state to have 15 consumer-run peer support centers, as well as mental health centers, to provide this kind of support. I have one WRAP trainee at the hospital who is constantly trying to get me on her side in her latest senseless battle with the hospital, most of which she initiates by purposely breaking policies and forcing them to come down on her. She thinks support means always agreeing with her reality. I tell her, "You've stopped seeing yourself as a victim of an illness and started seeing yourself as a victim of a hospital. Wouldn't it be better to take some personal responsibility and stop being a victim altogether? What are you getting out of all these senseless fights?" It took a long time for me to come to this realization with her, and start setting this limit, because my instinct is to support the client against the institution. She was exploiting that instinct, or trying to.

The point of all this is that a WRAP trainer never stops learning – improving his own recovery planning so he can help other people improve theirs. Every trainee is a new reality and a new set of challenges and possibilities. Anyone who doesn't understand the value of that kind of life's work should teach French grammar instead. ❧

5
Wrap as an Entranceway Into a House of Wellness

There are many ways to begin a journey of wellness. And perhaps the more entranceways one sees the more likely one is to want it, to feel it is possible. I have found WRAP to be an effective way to bring people together to share a personal journey. Since WRAP has been accepted as an evidence-based practice, providers give it a green light. Increasingly, mental health organizations are realizing that if they don't offer WRAP they are falling behind in what is becoming a major transformation of mental health service delivery in the United States. Peer support and peer-run services are becoming increasingly recognized as emerging best practice. Some call it practice-based evidence. People who understand recovery know what works. It takes years and much data, however, to garner sufficient evidence to "prove" it. What is less recognized is that when the WRAP Group ends and the plan is completed, the next chapter begins. Let me share a bit of my story and how I incorporate WRAP into my work and my life.

In October of 2003 I got a job as a Recovery Advocate/Educator. I was informed that I would go to WRAP Training that winter. Prior to going to Vermont I did the pre-requisite readings and my own WRAP plan. I didn't expect to learn much during this preparation phase. I mean, I had a master's degree in Clinical/Community Psychology and had been a very successful mental health worker for 25 years. I had developed a strong social support network and worked very hard on my own recovery for many years. What could I possibly learn from answering several questions and practicing the preliminary exercises? As it turned out, I did learn some things about myself. I saw a bigger picture of what I could do to further explore wellness by putting even more attention on it and by being increasingly thoughtful about how I take care of my body and my mind.

I spent five glorious winter days with Mary Ellen Copeland and about 20 other mental health providers from around the country who, like me, were getting certified as WRAP Support Group Facilitators. I couldn't tell who in our group had a mental health diagnosis and who didn't. Only one or two people openly disclosed this information in the first couple of days. I silently wondered, not daring to ask or to disclose myself. In some ways it didn't matter—we were all human beings, all here to learn. I felt an awkwardness in not knowing. I was curious. Who was like me? Who was a consumer/survivor? Who wasn't? Who was brave enough to disclose?

As trust developed, informal conversations about our mental health histories emerged. We talked about some of the challenges of disclosing our mental health histories or diagnoses with others, either at work or in our personal lives. One of my new (middle-aged) WRAP trainee buddies talked about how she had disclosed to her new boyfriend (back home), not her diagnosis but rather that sometimes she felt sad. That was easy for him to understand. She used normalizing language to describe the feelings she experienced, which in turn led him to talk about how he felt sad sometimes, too. Staying on the feeling level (without the labels) brought them closer. It was sweet. It was honest. No need to judge, label, categorize and perpetuate language that artificially separates us as human beings. We are emotional beings. Sometimes our emotions are strong and intense and that may scare people for a while. The feelings pass and we find our equilibrium again. All of us thought a lot about language that week. We thought about the importance of getting away from negative, stigmatizing language that fuels misunderstanding, mental health oppression, and the illusion that there is something wrong with us. The illusion that some people are ok and some aren't. As if the mind actually goes somewhere. It doesn't. It stays right there. Feelings go places but they eventually come home and find peace and quiet. Eventually. Well, at least that is what recovery seems to be about. In ways, it seems to be about going home. Finding one's heart, one's voice, one's mind and spirit, and knowing that we are okay.

Since that WRAP week in Vermont, almost three years ago, I have led several Recovery classes in which the focus is WRAP and Peer Support. The two processes enhance and reinforce one another. Currently I do 12-week classes, two hours each with a half-time break. We spend about half the time focused on WRAP, the other half on peer counseling. In addition to these classes I lead two ongoing drop-in recovery groups a week for people with a mental health and/or a substance abuse issue. Lessons learned from completing the WRAP process continually get worked on in the recovery group. In actuality, the learning is continuous. The WRAP is a springboard, one of a number of entranceways to wellness and healing.

The groups and classes keep getting better as my skills improve and I learn how to reach for others with my flexible thinking. Over time I have also grown more comfortable sharing insights about my own healing journey that seem meaningful and inspirational to others. It's hard to find the words to describe what it is like to give the gift of recovery to others. It is the most gratifying work I have ever done. This work is deeply personal, deeply transformational. I get paid to get in close with people and help them find their voice. Help them find new ways to understand their experiences and to see their self from a fresh perspective. There is a simple beauty in WRAP. We take time together to think about wellness-what does it feel like, how do you keep it? When you start to lose it, how do you get it back? We do this in a group, so you can't help but develop natural supports as the group process deepens and members reveal more and more about themselves. People who never met before become warm and friendly with one another in a short period of time.

I share examples from my own WRAP. The most frequent one I talk about is my primary trigger - when I perceive that someone is not listening to me. I hate that, particularly when it is an important conversation. I get so re-stimulated sometimes that the old recording starts running - feelings of invalidation and worthlessness invade my thinking. I am getting better at seeing the old recording for what it is, an unhealed hurt that I need to work on in a peer counseling session. I am learning that when I am treated in a disrespectful manner I can completely stay with that person, listening and knowing that s/he may be acting out their own old recordings of unresolved material. Perhaps it is a place where they were hurt or traumatized. It may be his or her way of unawarely asking for help or support or a peer counseling session! One indicator of recovery for me is when the trigger happens (I get treated disrespectfully or I am not listened to) but I don't get hooked and my mind continues to operate using my flexible intelligence and not even one ounce of self-doubt or negative thinking appears. I am learning to stay present in the moment and better distinguish my unresolved issues from the other person's unresolved issues. I continue to learn about how the way we were treated as young people is often the way we treat ourselves and others.

Some people in my WRAP/Peer Support class have great difficulty expressing how they feel. They are not used to focusing on this or they don't typically have a safe, quiet place where they are encouraged to notice their feelings. They have been numb for so many years. Isolated and alone for decades. Some say that the medications keep them from feeling, it keeps their head foggy. I see the fogginess. It is a barrier sometimes so thick that I can't seem to get through to the person, the human being underneath the fog. It breaks my heart to see what the system has done to people, but my job is to try and find them, to reach them. Typically, if they keep coming back, and they do, we get some breakthrough. Small steps, but they are really very large steps. If you haven't had a feeling for 10 or 20 years and you come to realize that you haven't — that is big. It's a good place to start; any place is a good place to start figuring out who you are.

On the other hand I see people whose faces light up. I will see people smile for the first time in months or years. The WRAP process teaches them that they are not alone, other people experience these triggers and feelings and take similar action steps to maintain wellness. People who have been coming to the clubhouse for 10-15 years suddenly begin to see one another in new ways, in deeper ways. They reach for each other in every group. They articulate their appreciation for one another. It is very meaningful and gratifying for all. They laugh and share stories about triggers and how they have been able to use these new techniques (action plans) to not beat themselves up as much as they used to. These tools help them feel better about themselves. They get new ideas about how they can get help and support. People are trying yoga and meditation and loving it! People learn how to develop a support network and to think about other members of the group as allies and resources for when they need someone to talk to.

In addition to doing WRAP, everybody enjoys peer counseling. Many find it awkward at first (as I did). They aren't used to being listened to and having someone's full, undivided attention. It contradicts the isolation that many people feel. Having someone pay attention to them is very validating of who they are as human beings. I encourage people to peer counsel every week between recovery classes and for the most part, they do. Some need encouragement. Some need to be matched up with a buddy. If they can't peer counsel face-to-face they do it on the phone. The peer counseling time is often used to reinforce and integrate the information they are learning by doing their WRAP. It provides an opportunity to focus on themselves with trusted peers and do deeper emotional work while developing trusting relationships.

The WRAP work and the peer counseling tools get revisited regularly in the recovery groups. In the beginning of the recovery group we pair off and do peer counseling. That way everyone gets good attention and gets to be listened to in every group. When someone needs more time I will give him or her a peer counseling session in front of the group. It is a way to demonstrate counseling techniques while supporting someone as they work on breaking free from an old recording. In some groups, each person (including the facilitator) gets to have a peer counseling session while group members listen attentively. It is hard to see the extent to which an unresolved recording has a grip on us. Often it is easier to see this process in other people. That is the focus of the group- liberation, freeing ourselves from old distress messages so that nothing holds us back from having the full life we want and deserve.

In the WRAP/Peer Support class, as well as in the recovery groups, people talk about how good it feels to have a place and to have tools that help them work on having happier, more meaningful lives. They talk about better recognizing their triggers, and how they take action instead of staying in the negative, angry or depressed place. They talk about gaining self-confidence, and learning to blossom, learning to reach out for other people and seek friendships, seek support when they need it. People talk about spending their life feeling lonely and isolated and now they know they have other people who care about them. And they care about other people and are learning to show it. They talk about knowing they have a safe place where they can come and be themselves, be with peers. They can talk or just listen or kick the punching bag. People share how they are taking charge of their lives and doing things they have never done before- like working out their anger in physical (exercise) ways, or getting on the metro and going to a museum by themselves, or speaking to groups of people about their recovery journey, or they share their 'secrets', like how they often start their day first thing in the morning by crying, alone at home. They talk about love and empowerment and feelings of anger, grief, missing deceased family members, wanting to improve relationships with siblings, wanting to find a job or volunteer work and where that gets hard. Most of all they talk about their recovery journey and we help each other take risks to show ourselves in new ways and to share our thinking, our challenges, and our successes. We learn with each other and from one another. We inspire each other and we talk about that too!

I share this story to illustrate how WRAP and other tools Mary Ellen Copeland has written about are much more than they may appear. It's not about attending groups, writing action plans or going through the motions. It is about recovery being a way to live your life. It is a lifelong journey of coming home to the person we were meant to be. It's about remembering our dreams and not letting anything get in the way of making those dreams into reality. It's about not settling for less than what we really want and deserve to have in our lifetime. These are precious tools and if we fully commit to using them, they will be transformative. And as we change and grow, we take people with us. Recovery does not happen in a vacuum. It takes a village. The village where I am heading looks nothing like the landscape of today. So please use these tools, because we need the entire village to reach out and transform the healthcare system, so that every person gets access to information and resources they need to live a full, gratifying, healthy life. 🐦

6
WRAP Stories—Facilitating WRAP

My life before WRAP was very scary, confusing, and out of control. I had begun speeding through life, failing at work, seeing and hearing things that others didn't, and spending money I didn't have. My friends suddenly seemed like enemies, confronting me with the realities of my thoughts and behaviors. They demanded that I go to the hospital to get help. Recovery was a concept that was foreign to me during the first year of my illness. I was expected to take my medications and follow orders from others, and to behave myself, or I would be given even more medicine. Two years later I heard about WRAP, took a WRAP class and began to see ways that I might begin to recover.

Working my WRAP has brought me a quality of life that I could not imagine as I sat in institutions for a year after my diagnosis of a mood disorder. I soon viewed WRAP as a career path for me, a way to help others with their recovery as I continued to work on my own.

I have now facilitated many WRAP classes with people with mental and physical health challenges. Through this process I have learned that I must take care of myself first. If I am not in good shape, I am not a good facilitator. Sometimes this is a fine balance. Along with my psychological challenges, I have numerous physical problems. This all affects how I feel. Sometimes it is clear I need to cancel a class, or get my co-facilitator to do it. Other times I feel sort of OK but not too great. I have found that teaching during these times is usually helpful for me as well as for the participants. I become focused on helping others, and others get a chance to see me as a vulnerable person who is also dealing with my own issues. It helps level the playing field. My challenge of managing Type 1 diabetes is one I usually share with the groups I facilitate. If my blood sugar drops too low during a class, I temporarily lose my ability to be on top of my game. I tell the class how I might act if my blood sugar is getting low, and ask them to please tell me if they think that might be happening. Often I get very pale. This is something I can't observe but others can let me know, and I can begin treating the hypoglycemia. I also lose my sense of humor, talk very slowly and have a hard time putting thoughts together. I may get irritable and sarcastic, ways I certainly don't want to be acting in class. In this process of sharing, I am role modeling taking responsibility, educating others, and soliciting support from my peers. I am sharing my vulnerabilities, making it a safer atmosphere for them to share theirs.

WRAP talks about everyone having the potential to recover, so we must assume that we all can take steps toward recovery. I have learned the truth of this, and try to never underestimate what people can do in their own behalf. I remember one WRAP participant who was very quiet, often contributing only a word or two. One day we were practicing origami as a diversionary activity. He got extremely focused and surprised all of us with his success in making his piece. He asked for more paper and continued to work hard even after the class was over. He showed us one of his talents and felt better about himself. Another fellow never came to our formal classes, but when it came to digging up some earth to plant a garden, he was right there with a shovel working hard. We each learn and participate differently. The variety of wellness tools in WRAP and the individuality of each plan allows us all to shine.

In another group, we started talking about pets, since I bring my service dog to class and everyone loves it as he goes around the group checking on everyone. One man, again someone who usually doesn't contribute much verbally and can neither read nor write, mentioned that he has a pet guinea pig. We all started to ask questions about her, and he opened up like a beautiful rose as he told us all about her. There were lots of funny stories, and soon we were all being very silly imagining his guinea pig being trained to ride on top of my poodle, and perhaps a mouse riding on the guinea pig. Although this man would like to have a dog, he realizes that with his severe respiratory problems, he would not be able to walk a dog, and instead has chosen a perfect companion to bring him joy and lift his depression I felt very gifted to see his broad smile and hear his strong laughter.

I have been teaching WRAP with a co-facilitator at 2 facilities for several years. Occasionally we take a break, but generally attendees at both places know to expect a WRAP class every week. These groups are an integral part of the programming at both places. A flow of content that works well is to spend about 12 one-hour classes on all the basic parts of WRAP. We incorporate wellness tools along the way. Next we spend several weeks practicing a variety of wellness tools. Peer counseling, journaling and diversionary activities seem to work especially well. Then we review the parts of the WRAP, encouraging people to write down their WRAP so they have a handy reference. This is especially important for the Crisis and Post-Crisis plans. The next stage is to start a Work Our WRAP group. We each focus on a relevant part of our WRAP, and share with the group what we plan to work on for the next week. Then we get together and talk about how our plan worked and discuss any modifications we want to make in our WRAPs. Both of these facilities are happy to have us teach these classes on an on-going basis, and see how their clients get better.

I have also taught WRAP as part of a professionally facilitated bipolar group that I attend as a member. When I teach WRAP it is usually for about 20 minutes of a 2-hour group, and comes first after check-in. This can provide a framework for people to hang their stories on, and come up with ideas of new behaviors to try. The group meets weekly, and I have a standing agreement with the therapist that if I don't feel up to it, I am under no pressure to teach on any particular day. I find that when we use the structure of WRAP, people become unstuck. Instead of just going over problems, they begin to take responsibility for their recovery, to take steps to change their lives and to build a strong support system within the group.

As a WRAP facilitator, and as of March 2006 as Advanced Facilitator, I find myself surprised, disheartened and humbled when one of our leadership, who seems to be doing so well, suddenly experiences relapse, and has symptoms that prevent her/him from teaching for a while. I am reminded that facilitating WRAP is hard work. We need to be self-reflective and pro-active in our own recovery. We are peers with all the same stresses as others with mental health challenges, as well as the stresses of being a leader, a role model. We all have our own triggers and deal with all sorts of others who have theirs, too. We care deeply about helping others or we wouldn't have chosen this line of work. We all need to know our boundaries and limits as well as our strengths. I think back to the role modeling Mary Ellen Copeland offered my group of Advanced WRAP Facilitators training. She was pulling back to take better care of herself after living under too much stress for too long. At first I was disappointed and felt a little cheated that she would not be one of the facilitators for our training, but then I realized the much greater gift of role modeling, taking care of ourselves first. What a powerful thing to do and share with us. I remember her words often when I start to feel overextended.

Since I can only speak from my own personal experience, let me tell you about the relapse I had in 2003. What a surprise, I thought with WRAP I had it all under control. At this time I found myself overwhelmed with taking care of all my physical and emotional challenges. I had been managing my diabetes for 44 years. I wanted a vacation, and welcomed into my life someone who would take care of me. I made a poor choice of people and ended up with someone who took over all control of me. I even willingly signed over my power of attorney for medical and financial decisions to her. Soon I realized I was trapped in an abusive relationship, and was kept from friends and family who knew me much better and cared deeply for me. Fortunately they fought for contact with me and provided vital support. Even though I was the one being abused, it was I who was committed to treatment in the state hospital for several months. Where was my WRAP? Why had I relapsed? Of course working WRAP is no guarantee we won't have relapses, or we wouldn't need our crisis and post-crisis plans. I learned a lot from going through this crisis, and pray I will not have to go through another. It is strong motivation to work my plan daily. I need to stay close and honest with my true friends, family and professionals who believe in and support my recovery. I need to share my problems without shame. I need to catch problems early. For me, one night of poor sleep requires action, and large fluctuations in blood sugars need to be acted on immediately. Mini-vacations are a must: walking my dog, watching a good movie, having a meal with a friend. I need to have an updated crisis plan in the hands of my friends, family and health care providers. Because of my personal circumstances, I am particularly vulnerable to wanting to be taken care of during times of stress. I have seen how this can backfire, and am cautious to maintain a healthy amount of interdependence. I did not have a crisis plan with appropriate powers of attorney in the right hands, and quickly got swept away in spite of my experience with WRAP.

I think because of the heavy responsibilities we carry as WRAP facilitators, it is that much more critical that we devote significant time to working our own WRAP. It is especially important that we share deeply with other facilitators who understand the same stresses. We may be more rather than less vulnerable to relapses. I am totally convinced that WRAP works if we work it. 🐦

7
Facilitating WRAP Groups:
Rubber Meets the Road

When I attended my first WRAP facilitator training in early spring in Brattleboro VT, I was in the midst of a major depression. My depression was so profound I did not realize its enormity until I returned home. Back home I began to see clearly what was happening, and gained a clearer perspective from the information I had learned. A sad irony is that two months prior to attending the training, I had made a serious suicide attempt, and a friend of mine had successfully suicided four weeks prior to the training. My life was a wreck. The WRAP training forced me to realize this painful reality, but the training also gave me hope. I had a sense of connection with other individuals who had comparable experiences. These people were able to facilitate groups in spite of, and because of, these very similar challenges.

I live in a beautiful place, however, there is little understanding of the recovery process. I struggled to garner support for WRAP. Even the organization that helped to fund my trip was skeptical that people with psychiatric difficulties could lead successful and productive lives. After many months of hitting brick walls I stopped trying—for a while. I had created a WRAP on my computer. When my computer crashed, I lost my plan. I did not create another one for a long time.

A year and a half later, I had the opportunity to attend another WRAP facilitator training in Brattleboro. Once again, my life was in a major transition. I had survived a bout with cancer; discovered that I had a genetic cancer predisposition, which could cut my life very short; and had just recovered from three major surgeries. This training occurred just when Mary Ellen had stepped down as Executive Director of the Copeland Center and Stephen Pocklington's tenure had literally just begun. Learning of Mary Ellen's genetic predisposition for heart troubles was as saddening as it was encouraging. In spite of her illnesses, Mary Ellen was continuing to participate to the best of her ability in this training. And, Mary Ellen continued to care about each person learning the newer methods of facilitation.

Returning from this sojourn east, I was determined to make WRAP happen in my remote area. I talked with the Director of the Mental Health Branch. He agreed to fund a room by the ocean for six months, as well as purchase ten *WRAP and Peer Support* books by Mary Ellen and Sherry Mead. This, in itself, was a coup.

I started truly facilitating WRAP in January of 2006. It has been a life saving process. Each group lasts for three months. The cohesion and support within the groups has been an important part of not only writing down my WRAP plan, but utilizing it as well. I could not be a hypocrite; I could not teach a process that I did not utilize. For me, this is when the rubber met the road. I am grateful that it did.

The first group was remarkable. Everyone who started with the group, save one person, ended with the group. This provided a chance to gain trust in one another and in me as their facilitator. Plus, I could learn to trust them in many different ways. The experience for everyone was beneficial far beyond the creation of a WRAP. The group was eager to learn, eager to share, and eager to support one another, including me. As the group progressed in making their WRAPs, so did I. Because I believe the group deserves to know my foibles as a facilitator, and that I too struggle, I informed them that, as they were creating their plans, I was re-creating mine. I remained one or two steps ahead of the group. This way, I could explain the benefits and challenges each category presents.

One member in the first group had trouble with worrying. When talking about internal triggers, this person came up with this understanding: Worry is a projection of a negative outcome. The statement was so simple, yet so profound, I have shared it with friends, fellow staff members and other WRAP groups. My first WRAP group as a certified Copeland Center facilitator was extraordinary in many ways. The participants taught me perhaps more than I taught them.

The second group I facilitated was more challenging yet equally rewarding. Several members from the first group decided to return as mentors for the new group. This was a way for these individuals to continue learning about WRAP, as well as help others learning the process.

During this group, it became apparent that one participant was in an abusive relationship. This was very difficult for me. My own abuse issues began to run rampant in my head. During this time I was grateful to have my WRAP plan complete and in action. I had gotten to the crisis stage in short order, but I knew where I was and more importantly, I knew how to get out of it. My WRAP plan helped my through this difficult time. I wanted to support this woman and her child; I needed to report the abuse; and I needed to get support for myself around all of these challenges. Too, I needed to maintain confidentiality for this woman, except for the CWS report. It was a balancing act, but I had the tools to work through it and came out successfully on the other end.

I am in my third group and I have one mentor who is a carry-over from the first group and two from the second. All three are acting as mentors to this new group, which is a larger group with about eight members. This group is as eclectic as the other two. Several members were very hesitant about returning after the first session, but they did. WRAP provides a focus on wellness. On the other hand, the mental health system in my county assigns greater attention to illness, while the WRAP perspective gives a refreshing and invigorating approach to life.

As a WRAP facilitator, I am grateful for the diversity the groups present. Plus, the many lessons the members teach me as I teach them about wellness and recovery is a gift. What a process – everyone wins in the end (or a new beginning). ෬

8

I don't think of WRAP ideally as something that can be taught, it's a process of self-learning. This is what makes it so difficult for people from conventional educational backgrounds to understand. A WRAP facilitator does not teach, not in some overt manner like an instructor (not that instructing is bad), but it's teaching what one knows to develop skills. It's not about the process of individual thinking. It's not by rote and not force fed, but facilitates WRAP or suggests ideas and offers people a chance for finding new ideas, especially what works for them. Ideally, what a teacher is, is someone who draws out from within the truth that lies there for that individual. A teacher is a thought provoker, someone who suggests idea, thoughts that spark the inspiration for one to look within themselves to see what truth lies there, but no one can actually make a person do that. So a teacher looks towards each individual to see how they think, to see if they can find what that person needs to focus their attention on and see if they can guide them in the direction they naturally need to go. But a facilitator does not have to do that, all they have to do is organize a body of information that they have obtained, in memory, in text, in images, and present them to an audience in such a way that the audience is participating in creating ideas to work on, for themselves or others. It's both peer counseling and self-help, it's whatever works per individual. It's self-taught, it's also a very simple process but radically different from the standard educational process. It's a process that I feel is based on the essence of what education really is. It's not so much about information learned as it is about learning to learn for oneself what works for them. It's hard to separate the process of teaching from the process of facilitating, but I want to make it clear that though one does not have to be a licensed teacher, one does not have to be a licensed instructor, but could individually have the qualities of being a good teacher as well. To my mind having a license to teach is irrelevant. Part of the beauty of presenting WRAP is there's no license, no grading system, we all learn at our own pace in our own way. By working together for some there is more motivation, for others they can work alone. The beauty of it is each individual finds their own way to learn about recovery and what that means to them. ❧

9
WRAP and Recovery

I first learned about WRAP when a friend gave me a copy of the book Wellness Recovery Action Plan by Mary Ellen Copeland. I read the book in December of 2001. I had been in depression for about six months and was looking for a way to recovery. WRAP became my guide to a life of wellness and recovery.

WRAP awakened in me a desire to take personal responsibility for my recovery. I decided to educate myself about wellness and wellness tools. I found the web site www.mentalhealthrecovery.com and signed up for the correspondence course. Back then you corresponded with Mary Ellen and she guided my education about recovery and wellness.

Under her guidance I wrote my first WRAP.

I enjoyed the course and desired further training so in January 2002 I attended the WRAP Facilitator II Seminar in beautiful Brattleboro, Vermont. In the facilitator seminar my understanding of WRAP increased each day. I became very enthusiastic about my recovery using my WRAP. One day I asked Mary Ellen how I could make my WRAP a lifestyle, "How could I learn to live my WRAP?" She suggested taking time each morning to read my WRAP and think about how to use it in my recovery. I followed her advice and invested twenty minutes each morning getting to know my WRAP.

After I retuned from Vermont a bad cold developed into pneumonia. I was a cigarette smoker and quickly realized that pneumonia and cigarettes do not go together. I decided to use my WRAP to quit cigarettes and to recover from pneumonia. I used my WRAP by first adding to my list of what I am like when I am well that I was cigarette free. I listed all the "triggers" that preceded my "needing" a cigarette. I next wrote an action plan to help me when triggered. Using this plan, I became cigarette free and recovered from pneumonia. By defining myself when well as cigarette free I set a course to bring my life in line with my personal vision of wellness as described in my WRAP. This and other successes using WRAP helped my self-esteem to increase.

Again I used my WRAP to help me grow by showing my WRAP to my psychologist. I explained that the triggers listed in my WRAP cause me to suffer. I asked, "What can we do together to desensitize me to these triggers?" Over the next two years I revised and updated my WRAP to include the new wellness tools the psychologist showed me. Gradually I realized that some of my old triggers no longer bothered me. This further success gave me confidence in using my WRAP.

I have used my growing knowledge about WRAP to make changes in how I live. Most importantly, I have made it my personal mission to live in a way that I can obtain and maintain wellness. While I still have difficult times, they are less frequent, less severe and I recover faster. I have developed a personal daily plan to manage my life and I prioritize this plan each day to support my wellness. I have also made long-term goals that reflect my hopes and dreams. My study of my triggers continues to note new triggers as they occur and has guided me to develop action plans to reduce or eliminate suffering caused by triggers. I have become very familiar with my signs and symptoms that indicate a change in my wellness. In doing this, I have decided that some signs serve as an early warning for me. Some other signs, if they occur, mean that my situation is more serious and that I must take immediate action to return to wellness. Using WRAP this way has helped me to adopt hope as an enduring part of my life. Today I am more resilient and resourceful than before. WRAP has become a way of life for me. I use WRAP each day and also enjoy facilitating WRAP workshops and seminars. I am committed to bringing WRAP to our veterans and to the corrections systems.

I would never want to return to my life before I had a WRAP. I am much more happy now and enjoy life again. 🐦

10

I recently attended a WRAP training seminar in Brattleboro, VT to be certified as a facilitator of this program. Previously, in the Spring of '06 I took a 13-week course to learn how to write my own WRAP recovery plan.

I really benefited from the classes and began to incorporate what I had learned into my life. I am a psychiatric survivor who has suffered for many years with anxiety and depression. What I had begun to see over time, through my own healing work and journey, was that I made the same mental mistakes over and over, and most of the time I had the same results!! Though I felt quite well on my own healing path previous to WRAP, I knew I needed something more to piece parts of the puzzle together.

After my WRAP class I began to write daily in my notebook about triggers and recognized that when I am triggered I always reacted the same way, often with panic and anxiety. I would withdraw and treat myself like I was very fragile. Using my WRAP plan, I learned to talk to myself in my thoughts and realized, aha, I can still function quite well with my daily life, even when having symptoms. This was quite a metamorphosis for me. I must admit that I did not pay much attention to the rest of the WRAP process, ie. making a crisis plan, etc. In September I was offered the opportunity to go to Brattleboro and I jumped at the chance because I feel inside I have a gift to share with fellow sufferers.

What happened to me during that week actually has taken me a while to sort out. I got triggered big time by stories I heard from some of the people in attendance, and I realized that in order for me to fully function in a healthy way and teach this wonderful healing tool, I must work my WRAP plan fully and over a period of time until I feel confident that I am well enough to teach it. Currently I am working my plan, taking careful consideration of my own limitations and strengths. I am being very mindful about my own recovery. I am so very grateful to be where I am and I know in God's good time the opportunity will come along for me to share WRAP with others in our area. I have more confidence about my own mental health recovery and process than ever before. I am on a very low dosage of medication and for me, this is a blessing, as I have never felt well on medication, as I have a very sensitive system. Life is a journey and change is a process, not an event. I am so grateful for the blessings in my life which are abundant. I thank the WRAP program for helping me fit more of my puzzle together. 🐦

11

First, I want to qualify my need to have a Wellness Recovery Action Plan (WRAP). From about the age of 6, I was identified as "needing help". In less than seven years I had learned to let things outside of myself (medication, jail, law enforcement, mental health, and addictions) control my life. Inside of me was chaos, confusion and a plethora of unnamed feelings and no way to understand myself or what I wanted or needed. I let things outside of me run my life for 23 more years before I learned a different way of being, even though there were many kind people, and systems, trying to help me. My habit was to resist help and to run with the urges and chaos that landed me in all kinds of trouble.

I heard Mary Ellen speak in 1999. She was telling the story about herself and her mom, and the challenges in their lives, some of which were familiar to me. Finding a way to address their struggles eventually led them to helping others find a way in which to live with their own gifts and challenges. I was totally into what she was saying; she wasn't trying to put something on me and she wasn't trying to sell me another piece of magic. She was sharing her story and what had worked for her. Just the idea that what was causing me so much confusion and trouble might be a "gift" was liberating.

What I got from her story was that I could find out about my own gifts and challenges and learn how to be with them. She said anyone could try WRAP for anything in their lives. I could take the action myself of finding out what I wanted and needed to be fully who I was/am, instead of continuing to react to outside sources trying to help me how they thought was best. I could know myself, and she offered tools to help with that daunting task.

I left that conference motivated to learn about a state of mind I found myself in sometimes, where every thing was a jumble and I was at the mercy of my urges and impulses. I had been told that that was mental illness. (I had already worked through my addictions with the AA, NA community.) I bought a little red book (WRAP) and began my own journey of Self discovery. I started defining for myself what Hope, Personal Responsibility, Education, Self-Advocacy and Support meant. Just having my own definition of those few words helped me to continue through the plan.

Using the tools I discovered I had through WRAP, I connected to the source of my Being. I was able to reach down and pull out this great person I had been afraid to share with the world. I have gone so deep using this tool that I believe anyone can use it to discover who they truly are. My personal experience of empowerment and accountability, how my life has completely shifted and turned around, has given me great faith in WRAP and in human beings.

I spent a few years refining my WRAP (an on-going process), and becoming a Recovery Educator for WRAP. I have run groups and trained others to use WRAP in groups. I have trained people how to train people in WRAP. I continue to do this work because in sharing it, I continue to know myself more fully and I gain new tools to help myself in even more ways.

There are three venues I have done WRAP groups in that have been particularly growth enhancing for me and, by their own stories, for the people in the groups. First, as an outreach worker for those defined as the "homeless and mentally ill", I did groups in the Public Library. Second, I did WRAP groups in the local jail with women who were incarcerated. Third is the experience of doing WRAP groups at a drop-in center.

As an outreach worker employed by County Mental Health, my job was to help people in the downtown area who looked "mentally ill and homeless." I had an idea about doing a 1-2 hour group every week at the library. I didn't push the group on anyone. I told my story, as I'd heard Mary Ellen tell hers, to as many potential group members as I could. After weeks of inviting people to come check it out, it began to happen. I learned about helping people I thought were in need of help, who didn't necessarily agree with that assessment. I learned not to judge others, to really hear what is being said, and not to just go by what my job wanted me to do.

One experience I had was with a woman who people viewed as defiant and disabled, because she was in a wheel chair and apparently living on the streets. I would say hello to her everyday, and she would respond. That was it. One day she stopped me to ask about the group. I answered her questions. She told me she didn't need that kind of help. We continued to greet each other. She kept hearing about the group from others who were attending. One day she showed up at the library to a group, sitting at a distance to listen in. It happened to be a small group that day; there was only one other person. I asked the group participant why he was homeless. The other lady, who had been listening quietly, startled me by breaking in, vehemently saying she was not homeless but houseless, and she wished that in the future people would acknowledge that. Then she left. The group ended and I went home.

My thoughts were spinning. All this time I had assumed that how I was defining people was how they would define themselves. Furthermore, how I was defining them presumed a particular problem, and that that needed solving. I assumed "homeless" people would want to write a WRAP to find out how not to be on the streets. Well, at the next group there were 3 people and I told them about what I had learned from the previous meeting. People began talking non-stop, about how people and agencies who have been trying to help them never ask what kind of help they need or want. This conversation opened a big door for me, and for many others. From that day forward, after telling my story, I always ask if people have anything in their lives they think WRAP might help them with.

I remember the first WRAP group I facilitated in the jail. I was a nervous wreck; I was going into a locked facility voluntarily, where I had once spent time involuntarily. I had to remind myself how different I was, how I now made empowering choices, how I knew what to do on a daily basis to take care of myself. That's what I would share with the women there. I went in, heard the doors lock behind me, and noticed my heart begin to beat more quickly. I took a deep breath and remembered why I had come.

I started not with WRAP, but with my story. But something was different about the story I told this time. I shared my story with laughter, hope, tears. I didn't make anyone or anything wrong for the things that had happened in my life, because I had come to accept that I was the one who had made the choices in my life, even if I hadn't known it at the time. When I was done I asked if there were questions. Hands shot up and the connection began. The first question was about why I would want to come back in here (jail). I looked at the group, took a deep breath, and said, "Because I remember saying that I would never go to jail again." Everyone laughed. I had landed.

I then told the story of meeting Mary Ellen, and what I had learned from her, which was WRAP. I shared how I had used WRAP to change my whole life. Participants asked questions and I didn't always give an answer. I would ask them questions to help them discover their own answers. Sometimes folks wouldn't know, but as time went on and they heard others share, they would learn. It took patience and practice for some of these women to get beyond their pride, and habit of blaming, in order to try a new choice and risk experiencing something that helped.

One day, two months or so into doing the groups, a problem the inmates were having amongst themselves in the jail became a discussion in group. When a high-ranking gang member came in, it changed the dynamics of the dorm. One of the women asked the others if, instead of returning to the gang dynamics, they could take this conflict to group to see if they could find a different solution. They all agreed. When the women arrived for group the next day it was so quiet you could have cut the air with a knife. I knew something was up then.

When everyone was seated and the guard had left, I asked, "What's up?" No one said a thing. There was a new person in the group, the high-ranking gang member. As she became aware of the nature of the group (it was not the 12-step group she had supposed), someone else explained to me the tension that now existed in the dorm, and here in the group, and their desire to find a new way of being with it. This was a huge risk and took a lot of courage and trust on the part of these women.

I told them I was willing to help them think through what had happened, help them figure out what triggers came up for them, and help them find some tools that they thought might be useful. We spent several weeks talking about the pressure that existed living in the jail, and how on a daily basis things could change from one extreme to the other. We talked about tools and choices that could be used in that venue. I learned with them that creating basic safety where they lived needed to be tended to before they could share personally. The group came up with tools and agreements and when that was finished, we were sometimes able to discuss personal wellness.

I have also experienced facilitating groups at the local drop-in center, where most of the population has been defined as either "dually diagnosed" or "homeless addicts who self-medicate." Stereotypes can polarize a group. In this group there's space for people to share how they wish, defining themselves, or not, in whatever way makes sense to them. A broad spectrum of people showed up to these groups.

I began by explaining how WRAP had helped me to make well choices in my life, and to depend less and less on wrap-around services. I started checking in with people about how they were living now. Most of them believed that if it weren't for their coordinator, or the system, that they wouldn't have even one day of wellness. We needed to begin with talking about simple things: how to balance check books, how to pay bills on time, living alone, taking meds, talking to doctors about what works and what doesn't work. We had to cover those basics before people felt empowered enough to know for themselves and to be able to articulate what they believed they needed.

I shared with them about having to take pills for heartburn; I didn't like taking the pills. But the pills were the only thing I knew that would work. One of the participants told me how she had found that eating an apple really helped her with her heartburn. I tried the apple, and it worked. I had a new tool and group members began to realize that they actually knew a lot, and had something valuable to share with others.

One of the big obstacles for these people was their habit of continually blaming providers for their level of wellness. We spent a lot of time talking about language and communication, how it could be advocating, empowering and useful within the mental health system. We explored what it was that the providers did that was helpful, what else they might be able to do, what could be different, how to advocate for oneself without anger, how to talk to doctors so that they hear us, and things like that.

I also found that it was useful with this group to start with a blank piece of paper on the wall and to ask questions. I call this the parking lot. At the beginning of group, people named what they were coming in with, what they wanted addressed. They saw it written down; it was not going to be forgotten. This seemed to help in a group that has a wide array of issues to address because of the broad spectrum of folks in the room with varying experiences. This has been a way to maintain the group through time.

Overall, I have learned that sometimes following the book as it is written may not be the best way to get a group engaged in their own process. People always want to know how to adapt WRAP to something that's going on in their life, in the present moment. I have learned that I really have to listen to know where I need to begin with any particular group of folks. The most important thing is for me to stay with myself and what I know, what has worked for me. I frequently find the best place to connect, because it's how I first connected to my own process, and seems to be a good way in for many others, is with having people define the five foundations (Hope, Personal Responsibility, Education, Self-Advocacy and Support) for themselves. ॐ

12

A Recovery Journey

When I was 17, my mother had her first breakdown, and was taken away in an ambulance. I was terrified she might never come back. When she returned, I vowed I would take care of her and help her stay in balance as best as I could. Unfortunately, I was no match for her mood disorder and she was in and out of the psychiatric ward until the final years of her life. Right before she died, she said to me, "You're my guardian angel -- you know just when I need you and you're always right there". Her words took away the guilt I had felt for so many years that I couldn't make her life happier.

Unfortunately in 1972, when I was 22, I had my first episode. I was misdiagnosed as a drug addict because I was having delusions and hallucinations. I was put in a state institution. No one would believe me that I hadn't been doing drugs, except my boyfriend. My parents were on the verge of probating me, which terrified me. I asked my boyfriend to elope with me so my parents wouldn't have the power to probate me, and on a weekend pass we went out of state and got married. I asked him many years later why he married me when I was in such a mess, and he said, "I saw a diamond in the rough." We've been married almost 36 loving years now.

I call the years between 1970 and 1980, my "Glory Years". I wasn't on any medication. I had two amazing children. I love being a mother more than anything I have ever done before in my life. I stayed home with the kids and when they were a little older, got part-time jobs.

In 1979 I started a business that lasted for 6 years. Then I worked at my sister's bookstore, and at an advertising agency. Between 1980 and 1990, I was in the psychiatric ward every year and a half or two.

It was the fall of 1990 and my world had come crashing around me again. I was standing in my room in the psychiatric unit of my local hospital. I remember thinking to myself, "I can't go on like this, not knowing when I am going to fall apart." That was my first step to recovery even though I didn't know it then.

Over the next few weeks, I reviewed my life and my approach to living. I discovered, much to my surprise, that even though I was a positive thinker for everyone else, I was a negative thinker on my own behalf. Every time I wanted to do something challenging on my own, I belittled myself and impeded my own progress. I embarked on a campaign to become a more positive thinker for myself. Each time I caught myself having a negative thought, I would change it to a positive thought. I could see results in a few weeks, but it took me about a year to really feel that positive thinking had become a more natural way of life. What a relief!

I also stopped going out for beers with my friends a few times a week. I thought I was doing it to relax, but it was actually bringing me down more than I realized. Once I felt more clear-headed, I was able to make positive choices better.

I noticed that when anyone asked me how I was doing after an episode, I would always say, "just fine". Because I was so humiliated, I tried to act as if my episodes had been a mistake. I really believe that always pretending that everything was just fine caused me to bottle up my real feelings. Later all those repressed feelings would explode regularly in the form of episodes. I was in dire need of a "Post Crisis Plan".

In 1992, I discovered journaling in a book called *The Artist's Way*, by Julia Cameron. Journaling has proved to be the most important way I connect with myself. It's how I work on problem solving, comfort myself, celebrate, support and encourage myself, identify hopes and dreams, discover patterns, and establish well-being. It is very empowering.

Along the way, I found support groups and became a facilitator, read books on mood disorders and other mental health topics, attended lectures, got information from the internet, and generally did everything I could every day to stay in balance. I started giving presentations on stress management, journaling, fairy gardening, and garden journaling. I even started writing a book on coping skills for people with mental health challenges. I also volunteered in the psychiatric ward at my local hospital. I discovered that fun and creativity are powerful forces for good, not just for people with mental health challenges, but for everyone.

In 2002, I went to a Depression Bipolar Support Alliance convention in Orlando, Florida. I met a person who told me about the Wellness Recovery Action Plan and I immediately knew I was hearing something very important. I liked each word – "Wellness" is a goal for all of us; "Recovery" is the path we all want to be on; and an "Action Plan" sounds like an empowering and logical way to get to wellness and recovery.

He invited me to attend a two day WRAP workshop and I knew by the middle of the first morning that not only was WRAP something that was going to be powerful in my own life, but that I wanted to learn how to teach it to other people. Soon I was traveling around Ohio giving WRAP overviews and workshops.

What struck me so strongly the day I took my first WRAP workshop was "What I'm Like When I'm Well". I made a list of 21 things – friendly, happy, confident, active, creative, hopeful, writing, cooking, walking, gardening, laughing, singing, and so on. I looked at that list and I almost cried because I realized that is who I really am. From that day forward, I started operating my life from a wellness viewpoint instead of feeling limited by the symptoms of my mood disorder. With WRAP, wellness is always just around the corner!

Meanwhile, I was going to Vermont to get as much training as I could in facilitating, and teaching others how to facilitate, and various other workshops. I even auditioned for and became a part of the Copeland Center for Wellness and Recovery and have traveled doing workshops around the country and in Canada.

I have met the most incredible people in this WRAP journey. From psychiatrists to homeless people. From Canadians to Floridians. I have heard their stories and watched as they've come alive to the promise of WRAP and with hope for their futures. When I have returned to do facilitators' training, I have witnessed some powerful changes in people's lives. The most common reason that someone wants to become a facilitator is that using WRAP has had such a terrific effect on their own life, that they want to share it with others.

My WRAP is an amazing friend. My "wellness toolbox" is an ever-expanding resource of good ideas that help me relax, be creative, and have fun. My "daily maintenance plan" assures that I have a good rhythm of healthy activities. When something negative happens, I understand that it is up to me to counter it with something positive. I am no longer a victim of my own circumstances. I don't feel foolish when I have "early warning sign." I used to think they were signs of weakness, and now I know they are simply indications that I need to take care of myself. I am glad to have a "crisis" and "post crisis" plan so my supporters will be able to follow my wishes if I ever need them in a time of crisis.

Having my family and close friends become supporters is a real blessing for me and for them, too! Before WRAP, when things were not going well, they didn't know how to approach me. Now they are part of my team and have the kind and direct language of WRAP to use when they reach out to me. I wish my mother could have had a system of supporters. Our family loved her, but we did not know how to reach her when things were not going well. As a result, we felt helpless as we saw her heading for crisis and ultimately into the hospital. I dedicate my recovery work to her.

WRAP is a true blessing in my life—to use and to teach. It is friendly, hopeful, accessible, logical, empowering, and kind. No wonder it is spreading around the world.

13
My WRAP Experience, "It Works!"

Monday morning, our group met with trepidation and excitement. Some of us knew each other, some were new faces.

Wellness Recovery Action Plan class for the week of April 10th - 14th! We had no idea, we were afraid, nervous, and I was so excited, manic to the max. Everyone who has taken the class will know the healing effects of this so brief time together. Friends reaffirming our strengths, admitting again our weaknesses. Strangers opening up, learning and sharing. You are not alone!

I had just spent the last three weeks frantically organizing, for the first time in my life, a WRAP class of 11 participants here. Many of our local businesses pitched in and supported our efforts with donations. Our instructors were from out of town. I had met with them the day before to set up the conference room we rented and give them the key.

The week went by like a speeding train. My brain was going through information overload, which means manic cycles for me. The #1 thing I learned, again, is—*listen*! Don't agree, don't disagree, don't try to problem solve, just hear, understand what the other person is saying.

We have a large binder with our class outline in it, flipping through reminds me of all the things I have read over the years from the *Living Without Depression and Manic Depression Workbook* (Copeland, 1994). This lifestyle works. Now we have a way to pass it on, in group form. "Each One Teach One!"

It is not easy opening up in front of strangers, but with a few friends in the group it helps. The tears did come, in many ways. I said on the second day "We're picking our scabs, making our wounds bleed so that they can Heal". I did not realize the truth of what I was saying. As the week went by too quickly, we created a phone tree. The WRAP class is not the beginning, nor the end, of a long journey. It is a vital part of the trip. Things happen. You can't change the past, but you can change your relationship with the past.

Options, Options, Options. When we meet as a group, we learn how others are coping, what their tools are. We find someone to Bowl with (yes we have one little bowling alley). Yet we are all tentative to step into someone's life, because we know we have "extreme personalities". The "normal" people can't handle us. So our future happiness is enlarged by the friends we make at these classes. Teachers who have been there, done that! Those are the professionals I look to for help. In my search I have finally found the answer.

We are smart creatures all of us, we can learn, and we can grow. Our process may be a slow one, but eventually we catch up with the rest of the world. We know how the world has treated us. We rise above the chaos and shine even brighter after being put through the fires of hell here on earth called Mental Health Services, and labeled a "consumer".

Now I have found my own answers… WRAP training is our future. Peer Support is the answer. I knew it all the time, I just did not know how to bring it about.

I'm looking at my workbook, and the first chapter with a check mark, wouldn't you know, is *Creating a Support Network*. Wow! I did it. *Using your Journal for Release*. Wow, I did that too! As I flip through, even the chapter on Peer Counseling is studied (I can tell, all my books are marked up). My favorite Panda bookmark (I'm obsessed with panda bears and purple and green) is on the page about SLEEP. This week during WRAP class, I hated getting up at (Good Lord) 7 a.m. I don't fall asleep until 5 a.m. naturally, and I live by my biological clock. Rather than fight it or push pills to help me sleep I just wait till my natural cycle runs its course. It works for me. I told my classmate I was going to be upset if I woke at 7 a.m. Saturday morning. And I didn't, slept until 8:30 a.m. By using my WRAP, I am learning to keep to my Morning Routine and schedule. I just can't afford to let anyone sabotage my Plan.

I went to the Annual Mental Health Leadership Conference in May 2006 (my 9th year), and worked my WRAP! I maintained control, assertively and respectfully specifying my rights, advocating for others in turmoil, networking with other WRAP graduates and instructors. On Thursday at 3:30 p.m. I gave my first presentation at a Conference. My friend taped it. I am impressed by the courage of individuals who boldly stepped up and shared their stories. Reviewing the tape for the 3rd time, I realize I gave a presentation outlining WRAP topics. When I got home, I started my morning routine the following Monday. Left the past where it belongs, and am moving forward.

Oh MY! The things that happen over time. "It Works," our Phone Tree is working. WRAP graduates continue to connect, network, support each other, and reach out to our Peers. Some of us have gotten involved in community activities such as Toastmasters, Saddle Up (Equine Therapy) and others. WRAP is a Life Saver! Our Class Bonded, with each other, as I have not seen in years from a group.

I was able to save money on this training week as we sought donations from the community. We hope that the Mental Health Trust Authority continues to see the infinite Value of this program, and continues to fund our Peer Support efforts. We are scheduling two more classes as the interest grows. With the tools I have gained from WRAP and Mary Ellen's workbooks over the last eight years, I have become a leader, mentor, WRAP Buddy, and much more.

A group of us are planning to open a behavioral health recovery center, creating a place to find peer-run, peer-support and advocacy for many who do not have access to the minuscule services available.

I have something to look forward to that will never diminish my self-esteem and integrity. I have Hope. I have Happiness. I am Content. I have a Future. We are having FUN with our WRAP. ❧

14
WRAP: The Journey

My journey with WRAP did not begin with a horror or "war" story. It began at a mental health conference in the early summer of 1999. Mary Ellen was the keynote speaker and as she talked about WRAP, how it began, what it was and how it affects one's life in so many ways, all I could think of was I need to know more and this is something that could change the lives of people who experience distressing symptoms and how do we get it going here. I nudged the executive director of the Consumer/Survivor Network of Minnesota in our state and said we have to get involved in WRAP. He looked at me and said, "Go for it, it's all yours." Little did I know where those few words would take me!

Facilitator training was the first step; trips to Vermont for the training, refresher training and peer support and WRAP training. All the while I was bringing back information and skills to the employees of our organization. Eventually WRAP was recognized by the Department of Human Services as an exemplary practice.

WRAP groups were on-going in all regions of the state. More and more people who receive mental health services were learning about WRAP and developing their own personal WRAP. It was changing lives, making lives better and giving people hope.

The more I facilitate WRAP groups the stronger my belief in WRAP becomes. I know that WRAP works, I am the evidence that it works, as are hundreds of others in our state.

I have several WRAPs, they are all a part of my life. On not so good days I check back to make sure I am doing all that I should. My Wellness Tools have changed as I have changed.

I began to work exclusively for The Copeland Center for Wellness and Recovery in 2005. Bringing WRAP, recovery and wellness to others around the country and in Canada was a dream come true. As I worked with people who received services, providers and family members it was incredible to observe their reactions, the recognition that there is hope—that recovery and wellness are not pipe dreams, but reality. The idea that there is choice, that they are experts on themselves, and that the WRAP is truly theirs and theirs alone, are life-changing realizations.

It is so awesome to bring recovery, wellness and WRAP information to others. Their appreciation and gratitude are often overwhelming, but I know how they feel. I had been there myself in the beginning. This work is so powerful, so full of hope, it is a joy to be a part of The Copeland Center and bring this work to any and all who choose to learn.

I have just completed (July 2006) one of the most satisfying, emotional and intense three and then five-day WRAP trainings. The participants were all staff from a medium security prison/hospital for men with a mental health diagnosis and a criminal conviction. Twenty men and women were ready to become change agents within the institution. They knew there had to be a better way to reach the inmates (yes, they are called inmates) and WRAP was going to be that way. By developing their own WRAP, the staff learned first-hand how awesome this tool for recovery is. In addition to their own WRAP, the group also developed a prototype WRAP for inmates. It is truly an incredible document, with a six-page (from an easel pad) list of possible wellness tools. On the last day of training, during the "Next Steps" segment, they set up a group meeting for August 3rd to begin the transformation process: meeting with other staff and administrators and making decisions as to which unit will be the first to have WRAP offered. Of all the programs available, this will be the only one that is completely voluntary. Two contact people were selected to keep me posted as to their progress and to be a resource if necessary. Their high energy level and strong belief in the power of WRAP to effect change is inspiring and awesome.

One staff person was very excited about having the WRAP available for those on the transition unit. The men on this unit will be released at some point and Jerry was convinced that if they had a WRAP it could make a real difference, maybe even keep them from returning. He was working on ways to present WRAP so that the men on the unit would want to develop a personal WRAP. During one of the breaks I worked with him to develop a community resource list to hand out to those leaving the institution.

Working within the confines of a very secure facility (we were locked in our training room) was somewhat overwhelming and a bit scary, yet the rewards turned out to be huge. I discovered that I actually enjoyed bringing the concepts of recovery, wellness and WRAP to a secure institution. I was also glad to leave each afternoon!

I never dreamed when I was listening to Mary Ellen in 1999 where my journey would take me. The opportunities, challenges and adventures have been incredible. I look forward to many more! ॐ

15

I first learned about WRAP at a local conference. I was affected by the testimonials that people shared and began to feel hope for the first time in many years. I was as high as a person can get just thinking that there was hope for a better life for myself and my family.

I have probably been depressed for my whole life and have had a very rough life with all kinds of abuse. But when I was 50 I had a major breakdown, was in the hospital for 55 days, had 11 electroshock treatments and was put on a lot of medicines. I was hospitalized several more times after that, never really getting any better. I am now diagnosed as bi-polar with PTSD, dissociation and the list goes on. But, I attended a WRAP class and then went on the Peer Support Specialist training and trained as a facilitator, and I'm here to tell you that I'm doing very, very well.

I do all the things "they" said I could never do: drive a car, hold a job, take care of my grandchildren, and most importantly, help others to see they too can live a full, meaningful and happy life. I love my job as a co-facilitator. I work teaching Wrap to PSR participants, and I also teach at the Mental Health Center. And I love my job, and it's wonderful to see so many people emerging from their shells because of what you've shown us we can do.

This doesn't begin to tell where I've been in the past or how far I've come to the present, but the future is bright! I have not had an episode for two years since I attended WRAP classes. I worked hard at it, and it works for you. It is so individualized and can help anyone with any problem. I think it will eventually be taught in every large corporation because it helps so much with self-esteem, and changing negative thoughts to positive thoughts, and making good choices, that it would help tremendously in absenteeism in the workplace. ❧

16

My WRAP Story

My home is in England and I am a WRAP Facilitator and Recovery Educator. My first personal experience of WRAP was in the 1990's to manage chronic physical pain and severe disablement caused by an accident. I had reached rock bottom, I could see no possible future, as I was then unable to walk. I was experiencing many other distressing symptoms with the loss of co-ordination, eyesight problems, memory lapses and constant pain. As a person who was always active, on the go, with my work, and involved in many community activities I found myself lost. I was always the one who supported others, had the right answers, solved the problems, yet here I was totally incapable of helping myself. I was struggling, drowning in a place that had no sense, no meaning.

I was usually a very bubbly, outgoing positive person who always managed to find a positive side, no matter how small, to focus on even in the most negative of experiences. Yet here I was asking myself... "If life is such pain what is the point of it?" WHY ME? I felt alone, afraid and completely hopeless and was thinking that what happens to me did not matter any more! I did not recognize this strange new person as myself, it was totally out of character, it was as if I had a permanent black shadow, I gave in and gave up. My life was over, my future was not just bleak, I had no future, it had evaporated away. I had the tremendous love, support and care of my husband, family and friends, but I could not at that time appreciate this.

To state that an event or experience changed or saved one's life sounds very dramatic, but the discovery of WRAP was my personal life-saver...it gave me back that first glimmer of hope. My illness and pain had become so all consuming I had shut everyone and everything out and surrendered to it. But here was a plan that I was able to adapt to address my own personal difficulties. As my needs changed, I changed my WRAP. This was my first tentative footstep towards my well-being and recovery, and I never looked back.

It was during this time that I was diagnosed with a mental illness, and later confirmed that I had a long-term serious mental illness. This was distressing to accept and hard to acknowledge. The symptoms are severe and debilitating. I could only be supported to manage the potential risk of my mental health disorder. That was it, ill for life, no hope.

I have always believed that something happens for a reason, and the finding of WRAP was there for me to use now, to prepare me to help with my mental health recovery. This was initially an extremely difficult, painful and challenging step as it called for total honesty, looking inside myself and not perhaps wanting to acknowledge what I was feeling or seeing. This was made all the more difficult for me as I had major gaps in my memory, in fact, there was almost nothing prior to 1997. I had to accept that this was all that I had to work with, my life was unknown to me, unmanageable, and out of my control. I began putting together my WRAP. I worked on this alone at first, getting my thoughts together. What did I want? What did I expect? What were my hopes for recovery? What were my goals and aims? What was realistic for me? Did I have the inner strength, faith and courage to begin this journey?

I had accepted the challenge and took recovery as my way forward, the approach to a new start in my life. I was looking to rediscovering myself on my personal journey towards wellness. I knew it would be a different me, as we can never return to what was previously. However, I realized that the stress of survival, lurching from one crisis to another, was damaging to both myself and my family. WRAP had successfully helped me to manage my physical problems, now it would help me to take back control of my mental health and accept responsibility for my life...and turn life's negative stumbling blocks into positive stepping stones.

It was a bumpy start. I was learning, educating myself to try and understand, and recognize, the severity and frequency of my distressing symptoms and experiences. Very difficult to achieve, as I have a severe dissociation disorder and have absolutely no recollection or knowledge of events during an episode of illness. I had to rely on others to fill in the gaps as I only held some pieces of the jigsaw puzzle.

I was in the driving seat, accepting responsibility for my wellbeing, making informed choices, taking positive risks and making decisions. When times were at their most difficult and challenging, holding onto HOPE and having the courage and strength to walk another step forward on my journey. I then understood the importance of being ready to embrace and make changes. This decision can only come from within the person when the time is right for them. Who knows us better than we know ourselves? Has it been an easy option? Most certainly not. I was realistic and acknowledged that it would not always be plain sailing. I have experienced setbacks along the way when my mental health disorder has escalated out of my control and I have learnt to accept that this may occur. The difference now is that I hold the tools to support my own recovery and my wellbeing.

My WRAP has many coats and I only hang onto the proven good elements. I bring in new things to work on my current circumstances and needs as my life moves along. It is very easy to fall into the "comfy old slippers syndrome," keeping the well-worn dog-eared WRAP and never changing the original. I check in with myself every morning to ensure that all is well. This for me is an integral part of my daily routine. Due to the nature of my personal mental health difficulties I use icons to put together my WRAP, as I may if extremely unwell be unable to verbally communicate. This enables my family, peers or mental health team to understand by my indicating the level of distress and the support that I may need at that time. This also requires a relationship of trust with peers chosen to support when things are tough going.

It is with a strong sense of purpose, courage of conviction, hope and belief in WRAP that I have over the years supported many people to develop their own WRAPs. It succeeds by the very nature of its simplicity, adaptable for any person to tailor to their unique personal needs. I am proud to have been a forerunner and major influence in WRAP and Recovery becoming everyday practice in services. I have facilitated many groups, large and small within the community around the country, and passing on my knowledge and first-hand experiences of using WRAP. I have supported many individuals on a one-to-one basis in acute in-patient settings, an intensive care ward (PICU) and in the community. Also people with learning disabilities, visual difficulties, deafness, those whose first language is not English, young people and older persons. WRAP does not discriminate, and I look for the best way to support each individual to develop their WRAP. I am currently looking at putting a WRAP together for older persons experiencing dementia in residential home setting. My husband, as my main supporter, has a WRAP. It is important that his needs are also acknowledged and recognized.

My personal philosophy: Recovery is not about finding a miracle cure or returning to how it used to be. It is about finding a better, healthier, whole-person approach to one's life. One that recognizes the past, accepts the possible limitations of the present And is full of HOPE for the future. Recovery is all about where I am going to...not where I am coming from. It is about the future...and making it the very best it can be, creating positive changes in any aspects of my life to achieve this. It is a unique, individual and personal journey of self-discovery, self-renewal and transformation. Using my own personal perspective, personal values, attitudes and reasons for wishing to make positive changes, my journey of recovery is continual, it is a part of my everyday life and sometimes I falter, but I have not failed, I still have my self-respect and self-determination.

> Do not follow where the path may lead,
> Go instead where there is no path
> AND LEAVE A TRAIL 🐦

17

I left all my friends and family and I moved to another state in early 2000 to start a high paying career at Computer Sciences Corp as a senior computer programmer/analyst. I got laid off at the end of 2002 due to outsourcing. It was then that my life started spiraling downward. I landed a series of lower paying menial jobs (selling lawn care treatments, a collector for Household Band, packing/receiving for Amazon.com etc.) and wasn't able to hold on to any of them for any length of time. In addition, my mother moved in with me after she got kicked out of her senior citizen apartment and that proved to be a burden, as I couldn't keep track of her medications or keep her mental state stable. I had to place her in a nursing home, which I still feel guilty about today.

Due to a blood disease, I had to put down 2 of my 4 young cats. Within a week, my car was stolen, I was evicted from my apartment and then, as the police came knocking on my door with warrants for outstanding assorted tickets, I went into a near diabetic coma with blood sugar levels close to 1000.

I now was homeless and was admitted to Wilmington Hospital for severe depression and mood disorder. I received eight electroshock treatments, which affected my short-term memory and gave me headaches. I was also diagnosed with colon cancer and promptly had surgery and two chemotherapy treatments.

At the hospital I met with an ombudsman from a non-profit agency and when I was released from the hospital they helped me file a Social Security disability claim, obtain group housing and meds.

When I eventually was given group housing after living in a homeless shelter for 6 months, I was offered WRAP training in Vermont. Up to the completion of the training my life was chaotic and hopeless. WRAP helped me organize my life more efficiently and live my life in a more healthy manner.

I had been facilitating WRAP groups for almost a year and the program has been received favorably, although consumers are sometimes reticent to write down the plan in their own WRAP binders but prefer to verbalize instead (as I write on a post-it board). Also we don't always have the same participants in each session, which leads to lack of continuity. In addition, two of the trained facilitators left the agency. So it's been a challenge. Facilitating others helps me open up about my own situation and serves as a growth opportunity. I now live in independent housing and take remedial computer courses at a local community college, although I miss not being in close proximity to friends and family, some who aren't too sympathetic with my plight. At least I'm basically functioning Okay on a day-to-day basis.

I draw on some wellness tools I've used when I was high functioning and see which ones are relevant today. Even though my computer job skill set isn't current, I placed my resume on the web to see if there are any non-stressful positions that I qualify for. I recently started playing bass guitar after a 5-year hiatus — playing music is creative and helps my focusing. One wellness tool which I would like to get back into again is stand-up comedy. I can't believe I performed in front of 50-75 people in New York City six or seven years ago. It was a very cathartic and creative experience turning near tragic events into comedy material. Taking a class helped. From these wellness tools, I try to keep my daily maintenance list which I try to adhere to. Exercising at the local Y, especially spinning class, is extremely important. Some things I need to work on are keeping my abode cleaner and a better diet, since I'm diabetic.

A larger section of the group has been devoted to external triggers (e.g. bills, legal problems, job search etc.) and the action plan. In the group I try to get the participants to open up about their own personal experiences, which are different than mine, and what are their own individual wellness tools and daily maintenance plan. ॐ

18

As a WRAP trainer for the last 4 years, I have worked with many individuals who suffered from mental illness. I also have had a personal struggle with depression and anxiety. As a result of using WRAP,

I have experienced a significant recovery from my own mental illness. WRAP contributed to my personal shift from illness to wellness. I have had the opportunity to share WRAP with many people who wanted to take responsibility for their own recovery and were receptive to using this tool to reduce their symptoms and to improve their quality of life.

It is hard to express my satisfaction as I witnessed men and women make real changes in their illness within a relatively short period of time, simply by using WRAP as a tool for recovery.

I believe passionately that the power of personal choice to educate and empower oneself cannot be overshadowed in the context of healing and recovery in light of the clinical emphasis on using pharmaceutical drugs.

WRAP offers a viable alternative for so many who are afflicted with mental illness and are overwhelmed with confusion, despair and hopelessness. Learning to use this tool can lead to personal power and transformation, from experiencing life as a victim to becoming someone who has a condition that can be positively altered. WRAP gives back some measure of control.

I believe that so many more people with mental illness could receive significant benefits if they were aware that this program existed and had the opportunity to participate in the process toward recovery.

With all the research and millions of dollars that are spent to find medications that will alleviate the symptoms of mental illness, surely more funds could be devoted to education and sharing WRAP program so that so many more people may receive benefit from it.

It is time that we shift our focus on how we approach the treatment of mental illness and realize that there is so much to be accomplished when we put our emphasis on what people can do for themselves by making a paradigm jump from dependency to self-empowerment. Not only can many more people improve the quality of their lives, we can also decrease the financial burden of treating mental illness. ❧

19
My WRAP Story

When I was 31 years of age I got married. I had been working for UPS as a driver for nearly three years. My job was to pick up and deliver air and international packages. When 9/11 came at the same time as a union strike, I lost my job.

Shortly after, I was offered a position as a prosumer (means person who receives mental health services and also works in the mental health system) at the mental health facility where I have received treatment for many years. During the early part of my employment at the center I attended a WRAP seminar at the local state hospital. I immediately felt a sense of direction in my life and a great deal of excitement. I was overwhelmed with a new-felt power of my life.

After a short time I attended my first WRAP group. I was inspired to learn more about WRAP and envisioned myself as a WRAP facilitator. My WRAP instructor was a force in my life that instilled the concept of the consumer movement. The clinical approach of recovery with contract and compliance were not mentioned here. I felt more comfortable in my role as a facilitator.

As time went on I took a training course in WRAP that lasted one week. With each WRAP group I became more comfortable in my role as a WRAP facilitator. I believe I had a foundation to practice and hone skills that enabled me to become a better group facilitator in my groups at the PSR center where I work today.

Eventually I became a full time employee at the center. My responsibilities have increased as well. I became a clinician type worker with 17 caseloads, which also entailed case management and documentation. In addition, I lead two to three groups per day. I even invented a new group called "music and you" which has become a favorite.

WRAP has taught me many things that I use in my recovery process today. For example, I like to carry mints, especially Altoids, because they help me breathe. I sometimes forget to breathe when I'm stressed.

I learned the concept of full spectrum lights. I have them at work and at home. I have developed an awareness of myself that I had not had before.

After working five years at the center, two as a clinician, I came to the conclusion that my anxiety was increasingly a problem for me. I realized that in order to care for myself I needed to make a change. I was offered a job as a public aid specialist. This position is less stressful and after learning this job I was asked to run WRAP groups in addition.

I would not have had the insight or self-preservation to make the change in positions if not for WRAP. In the WRAP plan I used Early Warning Signs and When Things are Breaking Down to make healthy decisions about life. I was lucky enough to be offered this new position.

WRAP has spurred me to become a more vital and purposeful person. After being involved in WRAP I have the empowering concept of recovery. I would like to think that I have helped others as well.

I would like to cite a time that I felt particularly grateful to be a WRAP facilitator. A middle-aged gentleman, now attending the PSR program, had been a recluse for much of his adult life. After being convinced to try PSR he was apprehensive about attending. He took the WRAP class. He then told his primary, "If I had heard these things before I would have been on the road to recovery a long time ago." ❧

20

I think there are several things to consider about doing WRAP classes that are targeted to people with dual diagnoses. Starting with how our values guide us, I'm sure we all try to make sure that everyone is welcome at the table and that people are accepted exactly as they are in their uniqueness, which to my mind means that I see only whole people and not diagnoses. Although it is not explicitly stated in our value statements, the power of language is clearly addressed in facilitator certification and it is clear that part of the facilitator role is to support class participants to move beyond the limitations of diagnoses and identities that are defined by labels or symptoms, but we do so without any unwelcome pushing.

Consequently, I would be very unlikely to set up a class specifically for people with dual diagnoses or any other set of labels, although I would facilitate a WRAP class for any group that invites me. If a group of people who have come together for mutual support around their shared struggles with any diagnosis or set of diagnoses invite me to facilitate a class for them, I would do so happily and without passing any judgments on either their group or individual identities. However, there wouldn't be anything different about the class except what the participants bring to the shared learning process. For me, every class is different in that way, and I see my role as facilitator to be one of bringing out the uniqueness of the individuals and the group. If it's somehow a dual-diagnosis flavored WRAP class, it will be because of what the participants bring to it.

I should probably acknowledge that my personal experience is both with mental health difficulties and substance use and the personal pleasure I derive from a WRAP class is diminished whenever the focus of the class seems to be one or the other, as opposed to holistic "wellness."

One person in the group made some wise comments about dual diagnosis classes, I want to suggest caution with using a phrase like "harmful practice." I know and respect her well enough to know that she would never wish to pass any judgments, but I want to encourage everyone to be careful not even to imply any judgment with a phrase like that. I can look back at my own experience with drug use and conclude that at times, and perhaps overall, it was a harmful practice, but my relationship with you will be damaged if you pass that judgment. The truth is that there were times when my drug use literally saved my life. It's a complex matter, and it's never our role to judge another person. And I think this points to one of the dangers of working with any fairly homogeneous group—because of all they have in common, such groups can easily slip into sweeping judgments that don't get challenged because they are shared, making the role of the facilitator even harder.

In response to another trainer's concerns about creating discomforts, the trainer showed that her actual approach is good. The simple truth is that facilitating involves a long series of difficult decisions, and no matter how or what you choose, people are going to feel differing degrees of discomfort, which, depending on one's personal degree of discomfort, is always a relatively good or difficult thing, and sometimes it's both. Your sensitivity to people's discomfort is what makes for being a good facilitator. You ask what you could do differently and I hope you get lots of feedback, but I also hope you don't think the feedback you get means you did anything wrong.

One of the things I do is to talk a bit about "discomfort" when I facilitate the creation of the comfort agreement. I ask people to think a bit about times in the past when they were able to sit with some discomfort in order to get or do something that really mattered to them. I encourage them to help us build an agreement that will let them feel safe enough that they will be able to sit with a bit of discomfort when it arises, and also build into the comfort agreement that if things get too uncomfortable, we can revisit the agreement... and, of course, I always make sure people know they can do what they need to do to take care of themselves... and it was great that you honored people for doing just that.

Another thing I try to do at those points when I anticipate some discomfort is to build in a choice, which allows the group to decide how we might handle such an exercise. I explain my reasons for doing it the way I propose, but, because this is a shared learning process (and I expect to learn as much as anyone else), I am truly open to alternatives. ৯৶

21
Teaching WRAP in 45 Minutes

My reaction to covering WRAP in 45 minutes is that it is like giving people a wine-tasting in an eyedropper.... An Overview is okay as long as people who want to "buy the bottle" have opportunities to take longer workshops or work with others who can guide the process of turning WRAP from notes they write in a three-ring binder to a new way of approaching recovery (and life).

The Overview is like advertising. It gets the word out. How else will people know that there is more to know? But I think what happens in many places is that the Overview is where it begins and ends. There's not enough time to work through all the parts of WRAP in any meaningful way. So we teach about WRAP but we fail to teach "WRAP."

There are people here in my area who are saying that WRAP doesn't work because the people who have taken classes in the past (Overviews) have not integrated WRAP into their lives in any meaningful way. Most have never even gone on to complete a WRAP course.

In my ongoing search for a metaphor about the value of a good WRAP facilitator, I was thinking that learning to create a WRAP is like learning to play a musical instrument. Consider these three scenarios...

Scenario 1 - External "Motivation"

Some people have absolutely no interest in becoming musicians, but they may have parents or others who believe it is in their best interest to learn to play a musical instrument. Sometimes, especially if they have an exceptionally good teacher, these people can develop their own internal motivation (see Scenario 2). But most will humor their parent by going to lessons while refusing to practice and eventually drop it altogether.

(Likewise, people who take WRAP because someone else thinks they should will resist learning and fail to see the value. A good facilitator may help some to find internal motivation, but unless it is their choice most will refuse to practice and will forget about it altogether.)

Scenario 2 - Internal "Motivation"

Some people love music and have natural musical talent — an ear for music. These people can pick up an instrument and learn it completely on their own. It is fascinating to think about the number of master musicians who can't read music.

(Likewise, some people can pick up the Red Book and "get it" so well that they can create a WRAP completely on their own and integrate it into their lives. I believe these people are rare — but they certainly are out there.)

Scenario 3 - Learned "Motivation"

Some people take lessons on a musical instrument. If they are persistent enough to be successful, they may become motivated to continue to learn and get better. Many people who learn to play a musical instrument have an instructor that models for them, guides them, and helps them to learn to play fairly well. But they have to be motivated to practice.

One who facilitates WRAP suggests ideas and offers people a chance for finding new ideas, especially what works for them. Ideally what a teacher is, is someone who draws out from within the truth that lies there for that individual. A teacher is a thought provoker, someone who suggests ideas, thoughts that spark the inspiration for one to look within themselves to see what truth lies there, but no one can actually make a person do that, so a teacher looks toward each individual to see how they think, to see if they can find what that person needs to focus their attention on, and see if they can guide them in the direction they naturally need to go.

Integrating WRAP into the Mental Health System

In this final chapter are the stories of people who have been so impressed by WRAP and convinced of its value that they have integrated it into the mental health system. You will learn about various strategies for doing this from people who have diverse roles in the system and who have a wide range of life experience. In this chapter, names and organizations will be included when appropriate.

1

West Virginia

Kathy Muscari

A decade ago I was a Gestalt therapist in a rural West Virginia community. It wasn't unusual to leave the office late or work weekends to honor people's schedules and their desire to share time and tell stories. I witnessed pain, joy, growth, and tears. Like them, I had a few emotions tucked away. My certificate-covered bookshelves held a couple of Copeland books. People found hope in the gathered suggestions for dealing with difficulties. There were routine requests for excerpts from dog-eared sections.

Opportunity knocked me into an innovative consumer-run network. My orientation began during a feverish grant-writing fest. Staff

173

looked at me, anticipating newcomer brilliance. I stammered over an idea to bring Mary Ellen and Wellness Recovery Action Planning to our state. "They won't fund that," I was told. "It'll never fly here." I took the challenge, and wrote my heart into a proposal. I also took a deep breath and dialed a number I found on the back of a little red WRAP book. Maybe someone would quote the cost of a visit from Mary Ellen herself—wishful thinking perhaps, but why not ask? A friendly female voice answered the phone, telling me she was washing up a few dishes while enjoying some flowers through the window. It was Mary Ellen.

West Virginia WRAP has been ongoing since that initial conversation and funded proposal. Mary Ellen and Ed trained West Virginia's first group of WRAP facilitators that same year. Expanding exponentially, West Virginia has since grown a team of caring facilitators. Many promote wellness nationally. All continue to learn and grow, applying the wisdom of their own WRAP experiences. People still have a desire to share time and tell stories. I've noticed a nice change … conversations are more often about living, learning, and helping out friends. I find myself smiling. ૭ঌ

2

Wellness Recovery Action Plans and Keystone Community Mental Health: A Recovery Journey

Pennsylvania

Editor: Kathyann Corl, *a Community Relations Coordinator for Keystone Community Mental Health, a mentor for a Recovery Specialist program (peer support), and a WRAP user.*

Our Story

Keystone Community Mental Health (KCMHS) is a part of Keystone Human Services that are based out of the city of Harrisburg in central Pennsylvania. The KCMHS serves approximately 700 individuals with severe mental illness throughout Pennsylvania and Maryland in a variety of settings providing: case management, supportive living, community residential programs, partial programs, educational programs and supported work settings.

Recovery Specialist Team

As Keystone began its own journey of recovery, we began looking for a tool that would allow individuals to have a sense of choice in an individual plan for their own recovery. This journey has included the development of peer support and having nine Recovery Specialists and Supervisors who now use WRAP as a common language to communicate.

In our group meetings, we have shared conversations about the use of different WRAP tools, from using a carved stone with sandalwood during presentations, to keeping an orange in a plastic bag in the freezer so that when the dissociation begins the orange can be taken out, and by focusing on the cold and the texture of the peel and then beginning to scratch at the peel and smell the scent of the orange, a person is able to begin focusing again.

Our opening question on our agenda is: "What are we doing to take care of ourselves?"

Through using an integrated peer support model throughout our services, the Recovery Specialists have had opportunities to discuss WRAP and recovery-based conversation in individual and small group settings.

Keystone Center Story Chambersburg, PA

At this program, WRAP is used for weekly discussions with their small groups. One individual from this program found WRAP a significant tool to stay with her recovery journey during hospitalization. Her story follows:

I am a 22-year-old violinist who is active in our county Stigma Busters. I am currently using the third edition of my WRAP project. It has been quite a journey of self-introspection, hard work. As much as the WRAP helps me now, there was a time when I didn't use it at all. I was embarrassed and ashamed. I thought that I was less of a person as I looked over my lists of triggers, signs of decompensation, early warning signs. Then my attitude toward the project changed. With the help of many members of my support team, I realized that my WRAP could be of great assistance. All of my helpers asked for copies of my work so that they could use it in times of crisis. They contended that it makes them more in tune with me when I'm not doing well. They were right. Now I can use my WRAP on my own, I look at my lists of coping skills, toolbox items, and response plan item items when I need to. I keep a structured schedule to keep me on track. In addition to lists and schedules, the name and number list of supporters from the Personal Crisis Plan has been a great way for me to keep my helpers on one sheet of paper. My latest hospitalization lasted for 6 months and I used some of that time to teach my peers how to construct their own WRAP. I am planning to make WRAP a legally binding document. After all, who is better able to create a treatment plan than the consumer him/herself?'

A Recovery Specialist's story:

In 1995, I experienced severe depression and could no longer hold down a job. I really didn't care if I lived or died. I took a slight overdose to just turn off my mind and sleep. I held many part-time jobs and lost them. My path of recovery is still riddled with many ups and downs. I can handle them with the correct doses of medication and therapy.

Being a Recovery Specialist is work where I meet many wonderful, intelligent people who have mental illnesses. I have come to see that I am supporting them by my home visits and working with them on their own Wellness Recovery Action Plan (WRAP). It is not all about the WRAP. The socialization of talking, visiting in a relaxed and safe setting, and knowing someone cares, allows individuals to open up to me. All of my people were anxious about working on the WRAP and found it overwhelming, but I assured them that we would take it at their own pace.

The most important aspect of the WRAP for the people I work with is the Toolbox. It is hard for them to think of things to write down but as we talked about how they are feeling and where they are in their lives, it becomes easier. I can't emphasize enough the need of talking through their feelings. In every case their WRAP Wellness Toolbox quickly fills up with many pertinent ideas using this method. We all find the Daily Maintenance List to be an essential part of each day. It is an excellent coping mechanism that, used daily, can lead to a new lifestyle.

Triggers are crucial to recovery. Together we were able to think of events that occurred either daily or occasionally and are harmful to their health and safety. Now they are using their Toolbox when the Triggers occur and it has been helpful to them in near crisis situations.

One individual had great success with the WRAP. Together we worked on it for three months. She was surprised by the inner strength she developed using the WRAP. She no longer feels depressed and withdrawn, she has developed a new friendship, she gets out of her apartment and goes to the social hall. She realized that she could use her family as a support system and still remain independent and take things one day at a time.

I am still working with my WRAP and find the Toolbox to be very helpful. I am more aware of the triggers that lead to extreme anxiety and depression. I can function, even on the bad days, because of my WRAP in my work. There is comfort in knowing that there are millions of people suffering from mental illness and through the WRAP, medications, and therapy, recovery happens.

Case Manager's Story

My involvement with WRAP has been a learning experience and a way to break through some of the walls that people have developed. I have introduced WRAP to the individuals I work with as a way to identify the triggers that cause hospitalizations and detox rehabilitations. I have now seen how WRAP works for each person differently. I was trained through Drexel and my instructor was able to send me the Post-Crisis Plan in Spanish. [Available at mentalhealthrecovery.com]

I have been fortunate to work with a person from Puerto Rico that came to the states last December. I did not think he would be interested in looking at WRAP because he needed to be hospitalized. This young man is 18 years old and had experienced significant childhood trauma.

The incidents that led to the hospitalization were a feeling of needing to brutalize his body while having a violent panic attack. He broke his hand in the process because he was so disgusted by what he saw in the mirror that he felt he needed to change it, and with force.

When I first showed the papers to him, he began to cry. He told me that he wished there would have been something like this in Puerto Rico because he felt he would have been able to work through/identify when things were going to the point of self hatred for what had happened to him, that if he just would have written down how he felt when he was feeling good and identified the few people who he has worked with here in the states and even at home, he would not have reconstructed his face with his fist in order to hide the pain.

He is now at a group home and keeps the packet we worked on in his desk drawer. He takes it out and reads through it when he feels overwhelmed with his emotions. He uses his WRAP to open up and talk with the staff and other peers in his community. He is making strides and has enrolled in a GED program. Without the tools that WRAP allows a person to see they possess, we as recovery-oriented caregivers could not appreciate all the strengths that he offers to us.

Summary

As Keystone continues to use WRAP individually and in small groups in our residential programs, Mental Health Professionals have now begun to use the Creating Wellness video and other recovery education materials with all direct care staff to enhance their understanding of mental illness and of the peer support program. ❧

3

Montana

My name is Vicki Stull. I live in Great Falls, Montana. I am a Wellness Recovery Action Plan (WRAP) user, facilitator and advanced trainer. Mary Ellen presented a workshop at a conference in Great Falls in 2000. I was just beginning to recover from a devastating major depressive episode that had lasted about two years. I had been told that I would never fully recover. However, I was determined that I was not going to end up dependent on the mental health system. The group Mary Ellen spoke to was primarily providers who were not very receptive to what she had to say, but for me it was like a bolt of lighting. For the first time someone was telling me that there was great hope that I could fully recover and lead a productive life again.

After the workshop, I enrolled in the correspondence course with her and built my WRAP. As I used it and became aware of my triggers and early warning signs, I discovered that I had much more control of my life and I began to grow as a person again. I built a daily maintenance plan that really works. I knew what I have to do to keep myself functioning well, but never had it clearly defined until I put my WRAP together.

In 2001 I went to Vermont and was trained as a WRAP facilitator. When I came back I was appointed to the Mental Health Oversight and Advisory Committee for the State of Montana and began working both to educate myself about recovery and the consumer movement and to get WRAP recognized as a program that could help the people of Montana who were experiencing difficulties in their lives.

Facilitating in Montana has been an uphill battle. With the help of the Mental Health Association I was able to do several workshops and each one was received with enthusiasm by the participants. They came out of the workshops with great hope and with new tools but with no real consistent support. They went right back into an environment where there was a total lack of understanding of what WRAP was or what communities of support were and no real way to stay connected to each other.

There has been growing support of consumer driven initiatives and the atmosphere has changed somewhat. In 2005 we did a video broadcast of the basic recovery principles to over 100 people watching from 23 different locations. Out of that group and video viewers of the broadcast we did three workshops, one in each of the service areas in Montana. It was in these workshops that things really began to happen. By this time, the State and others were more committed to recovery. We were able to help people see that with a WRAP plan, and support from the State and the Mental Health Association, there was a commitment to building a community of WRAP users and of consistent WRAP trainings and opportunities for review and advanced training. In May of 2006 we did another broadcast. This time we had over 300 participants, and we have six people from our workshops from last year going to a facilitators training that is being held in California. In April of this year I went back to Vermont for Advanced Training and am now prepared to train the trainers. Although we have sent this first group to California, we hope to be doing another facilitators training later in the year.

As a facilitator, there are three areas that I want to comment on. First is the growth of individuals that I have seen, second is the growth of the program in this state, its acceptance and use, and third are the problems that I have seen for both individuals and the program as WRAP and peer support has been pushed into the mental health system, by both state and national insistence, but without adequate preparation of the professionals or the community.

First: The growth of individuals. It has been exciting to see people come into a training and "get it". The "it" that they get is that they can make a difference in their own lives. They begin to see that others have overcome great difficulties to lead lives that are fulfilling and satisfying. That even when difficult times still trouble them, they can minimize those difficult times and make something good for themselves. I remember one person in one of the workshops last year was quiet. She participated, but was reserved and contemplative, and even though I couldn't really tell from her work in the group if she really "got it" or not, her comments were perceptive. At some point I looked at her and told her that I thought that her ability to analyze the situation and her depth of perception would come in handy if she chose to go on to facilitator training and that I thought she would make a good facilitator. I really didn't know how she would integrate the WRAP plan in her life. She went home and began using and revising her plan. She went to her voc rehab counselor and told them that she wanted to become a wellness educator and they put a program together for her to set up her own business. She went to her counselor and told her how she felt, what she was doing and what she wanted to do and that she felt like she now had the tools to keep herself in recovery. Her counselor laughed at her, kind of behind her back, but she got the picture that the counselor didn't believe her. Since that time she has gotten involved with a committee that is putting together a peer support specialist program and I have watched her set limits for herself and follow her WRAP to keep herself in recovery. She is one of the six that are heading to California for facilitator training. Although she liked her counselor and still uses her on occasion, she now sees that she is in charge and the counselor is a resource, but not the be-all, end-all of what she can or cannot do. She is debating how she is going to use the facilitator training because she knows that she could overload herself if she does not follow her plan. She also sees that the group that is trying to incorporate peer support into an existing mental health center framework is having trouble understanding what real peer support is all about. It has been great to be able to be at meetings with her. We have ended up being a support to each other.

One of the other people I particularly remember is a young man who is still struggling, but who took from the training a firm understanding that he had the right to ask his doctors for changes in the way he was being treated and expect that he would be listened too. He barely participated the first day and I thought that he wasn't getting a thing. About three weeks after the workshop, he came running up to me at the State Mental Health Conference, in front of the person who handles consumer affairs on the state level, and hugged me and thanked me for the class, and said, "You're never going to believe what happened. I learned in the WRAP class that I could talk to my doctor about what I wanted, so I told him that I thought I was on too much medication and that it was slowing me down and I wanted to get a job and I thought that less medication would make me less sluggish and could I try less medication. And, guess what, he thought it was a good idea. He really listened to me and dropped my med dose and I applied for a job at the truck stop and I am working half-time now." They were gathering stories at that conference and he went in and told his story. He was so excited about the fact that he had the right to ask for what he wanted and expect that others would respond. He is really just beginning on his journey and he may need another experience in class before he even starts to write his WRAP plan, but he has felt great hope and has been empowered to do things he had never thought of doing before.

Second: The growth of the program in this state. I have been teaching and advocating for WRAP sessions since 2001. However, we have had no real way to follow up, or to keep track of participants, or to help them find others to build peer relationships with. There was no structure. Last year the Montana Mental Health Association made WRAP training an educational priority and they began to handle the logistical stuff. It has made a huge difference and we are making steady progress.

WRAP has been a lifesaver for me. Because of it, I have been able to be active in professional life and as a WRAP facilitator. I have been able to monitor my life and incorporate time for myself with my family and friends. I can stop and take stock of what is going on around me and decide where I want to be in relationship to it instead of letting it over-whelm me. When I find myself being confronted by multiple priorities and spinning into thinking that I have to do it all, I can stop and not let myself go there. I feel so much more powerful in my own life. I no longer have to do something just because I know I can, I can choose where I want my energy to be expended. I have always believed that all people had something to offer me, and that I have something to offer them, but with WRAP I have been able to see how to expand and nurture mu-tually supportive and growth-enhancing relationships. It has fit so well into the worldview that I already had. As a facilitator, I have seen those same kinds of things happening in the lives of others.

4

"Wrappin' 'n' Wrollin" in Illinois

Nanette Larson

In May of 2002, three self-determined women ventured from Illinois to Vermont to complete the Recovery Education and Wellness Recovery Action Plan (WRAP) Facilitator's Training course with Mary Ellen Copeland. Later that month, the University of Illinois at Chicago (UIC), hosted a Self-Determination Workshop. Mary Ellen Copeland was one of the guest speakers for the Self-Determination Workshop, presenting a three-hour overview of WRAP to an eager and interested audience. Although unintentional, it was the coming together of these two events that led to the eventual formation of the Illinois WRAP Steering Committee and the resulting initiative now known as "Wrappin 'n' Wrollin' in Illinois!" What a joy it is to be able to share a bit of our story with you!

I was one of the participants at the Self-Determination Workshop; my position at the time: "Acting Director of Consumer Services" for the Department of Human Services (DHS)/Division of Mental Health (DMH). Having read a bit about WRAP, I came eager to learn more. But it was observing the impact that this simple, yet profound, presentation of recovery and WRAP had on the members of the audience, that truly had me sold. I could hardly contain my enthusiasm. Two of the women, Mary Jensen and Carol Vollendorf, who had been to Vermont, were colleagues of mine. They were there also, sharing in the energy. Also present was one of our DMH Network Managers, Dan Wasmer. His ebullience was just as evident. So there we stood, the four of us, on Michigan Avenue on a beautiful day in May, and we began to design the Illinois WRAP Steering Committee.

Our first event had to be planned quickly, as we wanted to build on the momentum of the Self-Determination Workshop. So, with less than three months to plan it, we scheduled a statewide event for August 2002. "Wrappin' 'n' Wrollin' in Illinois" was born! I will never forget the day I spoke with the DMH Director about this event. I handed her the brochure, still in draft form, to obtain her endorsement, and her first comment was, "I love the title!" We were fortunate to have the expertise of Charity Appel and Alan McNabb, trainers from The Copeland Center for Wellness And Recovery, for this day-and-a-half event. Over one-hundred people participated. Everyone who participated learned so much, and so did we!

One of the most significant things I learned, from the perspective of one who desired to see WRAP become a key element of service delivery in the overall mental health system, was how important it was to make distinctions between different levels of WRAP education. For example, persons who had attended the three-hour workshop in Chicago said they had been "trained in WRAP." Similarly, persons who attended the day-and-a-half workshop also said they had been "trained in WRAP." Most notably, the reference was intended to mean that they were now capable of facilitating WRAP groups. As a matter of fact, many people were sent to one or another of these workshops by a supervisor whose expectation was that they would return from the workshop, with the knowledge base necessary to begin running these groups. Of course, that level of training had not yet occurred in Illinois. This was not something our Committee had taken into consideration, but we took quick action to remedy this. To help clarify the distinction between different types of WRAP training, we developed what is known as the "Levels of WRAP Education" system. This system provides clear differentiation between the various educational opportunities, prerequisites, and what persons are qualified to do, once they have completed that level of education.

Of course, now that the levels of education had been defined, it was time to get the next level offered! In December 2002, we held our first weeklong "Mental Health Recovery Education and WRAP Facilitators" training! Mary Ellen Copeland and Ed Anthes were the Copeland Center trainers for this event. This was a landmark statewide training in Illinois, marking the beginning of what we refer to as our "two-by-two" journey. Being such a large state, we are divided into geographic regions. At that time, we were separated into nine distinct geographic areas. As the maximum capacity for our Facilitator's Training was twenty, that meant each area of the state could send two people, with the host site receiving the two additional spaces. The twenty graduates of that event were sent forth with the charge, "to make WRAP a reality" in the different areas of the state!

In February 2003, Carol Vollendorf and I flew to Arizona for a weeklong training on "Implementing WRAP and Recovery in Your Mental Health System." Through this outstanding training, we were able to see both that our "Levels of WRAP Education" system had great potential, with a bit of polishing, and that our "two-by-two" approach could also work, but only if we were able to provide a bit of coaching and mentoring for those Facilitators. The best news for us was that we were not without our own mentors: the Copeland Center, Meta Services, and CONTAC were all on board to help us in Illinois, achieve our dreams!

Two more Facilitators events were held in 2003. Both had the support of Kathy Muscari, CONTAC, being on site to help mentor and coach our teams. Those two events resulted in: forty new facilitators trained, two persons trained to begin WRAP on the Deaf/Hard of Hearing unit at one of the state hospitals, and the first person trained to begin a pilot for Teen WRAP in Illinois! With great humility, I was honored to accept the challenge of 'carrying the baton' for WRAP in Illinois at the end of that season, and in April, 2004, I had the privilege to participate in the National Speakers' Training and become a Senior Recovery Educator with the Copeland Center.

Since 2003, our state initiative has consisted of two Facilitator Training events each year, one for the Chicago area and one for Greater Illinois. Additionally, two Refresher events are held each year. The Refresher events provide new facilitators an opportunity to meet other facilitators in their area, and create opportunities for continuing education. A total of 164 facilitators have been trained across the state. Of those facilitators, over 50% regularly submit pre- and post-survey data for a statewide database to contribute to research concerning the impact of WRAP over time. In addition, a weekly telecoaching call is provided, free of charge, for all facilitators in the state. These calls provide facilitators access to continuing education and mutual support. Catherine Dalton facilitates these weekly calls.

Now, you must keep in mind that this story is being written from the perspective of one who desires to see recovery and WRAP become a key element of service delivery in the overall mental health system. In Illinois, the public mental health system consists of nine state hospitals, contracts with community hospital inpatient psychiatric units, and over 160 contracted community mental health centers. And, although training facilitators is an essential element, it is only one piece of the puzzle in achieving the dream. A large part of the work in the past year, therefore, has been focused on addressing major system changes necessary to see the dream realized. These range from changes in the Medicaid Rule for reimbursement, to changes in contract language that governs the state's relationship with community mental health agencies.

I close as I began. Chicago is indeed 'the windy city,' and the winds of change, with WRAP, continue. Most significantly, this year we began the process of regionalizing our WRAP Training, and several of our Recovery Educators, including Mary Jensen, Rhonda Keck and Carol Vollendorf, are doing great jobs coordinating events. Also, we are standardizing the certification process for Facilitators and Recovery Educators, and are well on our way to further legitimizing this emerging best practice. With the ongoing support of our DMH Director, Lorrie Jones, and Chief of Staff, Bob Vyverberg, we feel our positive outcomes have been considerable. And as I continue to tell our team,

"We're always 'Wrappin' 'n' Wrollin' in Illinois!" ৯৺

5

Vermont

Linda Corey

WRAP was first started in Vermont after a recovery education cycle in Bradford, Vermont. A group of peers worked with Mary Ellen to develop a structure for incorporating all the recovery information they had learned and intended to use. The WRAP plan came to life. Today, as we know, it is used all over as a tool in recovery.

Initially, Vermont Psychiatric Survivors (VPS), a statewide recovery group, funded their recovery education through a pilot grant through the state Department of Mental Health. It was evident that recovery was well received by peers and by professionals as well. Early on, one county actually developed a recovery document to set up recovery oriented programs throughout the community. This was Washington County.

The next funding source was a three-year grant from the van Ameringen Foundation in New York. With this grant, recovery education cycles were offered throughout the state and 35 educators were trained to provide the training. They were done with a professional and a peer teaching together. They are still done this way in most of the cycles.

For the past six years, VPS has received Statewide Network Grants through the Substance Abuse Mental Health Services Administration (SAMHSA). These grants had line items to provide WRAP and also fund a Recovery Coordinator. It was also to develop peer leadership and peer programs. Presently there are 67 recovery educators and over 3000 people that have been involved with some stage of WRAP, whether through support groups, formal training or community presentations. There are WRAP groups weekly at both the state hospital and Brattleboro Retreat, a private psychiatric treatment center in southern Vermont. WRAP has been introduced in the Veteran's Hospital and through Veteran Support Groups throughout Vermont as well.

In Vermont, Mary Ellen is our curriculum coordinator and the state recovery program follows the ethics and principles of WRAP as it was created.

As for evidence, ask the people involved. Many have gone on to employment opportunities, back for higher education and also serve on many committees and boards.

One thing that acts as an incentive for others to try new things is the continuous story telling by people in recovery. It provides hope that people can move forward and are not destined to living their lives as they know it now. ❧

6
META and WRAP

Arizona

The history of META Services, now known as Recovery Innova-
tions, is rich with stories of hope and recovery. A key ingredient in
our evolution has been our involvement with The Copland Center for
Wellness and Recovery, and WRAP. Here's how it came about.

We first became aware of WRAP in 1999, when we were looking
for information on recovery, and we found Mary Ellen's web site, men-
talhealthrecovery.com. After reading the story of Kate, we were on the
phone making reservations for a week in Brattleboro. Four of us spent
a week there learning about WRAP and how it could be used to help
people in their recovery. Mary Ellen and her staff were very supportive
of our commitment to bring recovery to Arizona. We left Brattleboro
filled with hope and enthusiasm for what we could bring to our community, and we were especially excited about putting our new WRAP
knowledge to work.

When we got back to Arizona, we introduced the WRAP to our
funding source and asked for funding to make it available throughout
our county. At the time, they had decided to only fund new programs
that qualified as "evidence based practice," so they declined our offer to
introduce and spread the word about WRAP.

Needless to say, we were very disappointed. It was terribly painful to know about something that could make a big difference, yet not
have a way to put it into action. After many troubled conversations, we
decided to try and do it anyway. So with no additional funding, and no
local support for our efforts, we started. A lot of our work initially was
just with one person at a time – someone who was interested and willing
to work with us on something called a WRAP that we promised would

make a difference in their life. This is an important part of our story to keep in mind, because it shows that sometimes, when your commitment is strong enough, you can start the ball rolling without any help, and because it is "right," people will resonate with it and it can grow beyond your wildest dreams.

Without any new resources, we were left to try and fit in a WRAP session here and there with those who were willing to learn about it. After three months, we had about 12 people who had completed the WRAP, so we decided to have a graduation to celebrate. We bought a cake and some balloons, and we asked some of our newly hired Peer Support Specialists to be our special graduation speakers.

Our Peer Support Specialists were very inspiring speakers. They told their personal stories about developing their own WRAP, and about completing the Peer Support Training and now going to work. Then the people who had completed their WRAP training told how WRAP had already changed the way they related to themselves and to each other. As we listened, we were more convinced than ever that we were on the right track.

One of the WRAP graduates told us that she learned to do the WRAP from one of us when she was at the Crisis Center. She told us that she had already decided to commit suicide as soon as she was re-leased from the center. In fact, she only agreed to do the WRAP because she thought it would help her get out sooner so she could carry through with her plan. But once she did her WRAP and started using it, her life began to change. She was now back with her family and back at work, and her life was on track. She realized she could manage a lot of her symptoms, and had a whole new outlook on her life.

An emotional father who was reluctantly attending the graduation stood up and shared his utter amazement with us. After his son had talked about how WRAP had given him the confidence to go back to school, the father said, "This is the first time I've ever heard my son speak a complete sentence."

This graduation was a galvanizing moment for META as an organization. We realized that we were on the right track using WRAP, and we decided that we would continue to offer it to anyone who wanted to participate even if we had no resources to do it. We would figure out how to do it, even if it was on our own personal time. We made this commitment because we could see that it worked for people, and it helped build a foundation for recovery.

After a few months we again approached our funding source, requesting they rethink our request. This time we took some video clips of people talking about how excited they were to have an opportunity to recover, and how WRAP had played a defining role in the process. We couldn't tell if seeing video clips was convincing. They said they'd think about it. About a month later they called and asked us if we could teach WRAP classes in nine of the case management clinic sites. We said yes.

We had graduated about 25 people from our Peer Support Training class at this point, so now that we had this new opportunity to spread the word about WRAP, we trained them how to be WRAP facilitators, and we invested in laptops and projectors for each team so they could follow the content in a way that had integrity to the concepts Mary Ellen had developed. Yes, we got some flack for this, but it died down pretty quickly, and in retrospect, it was worth the investment and the flack to equip our facilitators with good tools to work with.

A month later our WRAP facilitators were on the ground in the nine clinic sites with their laptops, projectors, snacks, WRAP booklets, and lots of hope and enthusiasm. Since they had already completed a 70 hour Peer Employment Training course, plus their WRAP facilitator's class, they were well trained and eager to make a difference. We had trained one or two people who worked at each of the clinic sites to help "open doors" for the facilitators, which turned out to be a very helpful ingredient, since they were there to explain to the skeptics what WRAP was about and who the facilitators were. The classes got off to a slow start. It took a lot of work on the part of the peer support specialist to round up people for the classes. They had to be shining examples of recovery in order to get others interested in attending. They would talk to people in the lobby, chat with people who were outside waiting for a ride, entice others into the classes with snacks and good humor. Once they were able to get people into the class and hear the content, the hard part was, for the most part, over. People were hungry to learn about recovery, and to learn that WRAP was a place to begin the process. We gave our facilitators lots of support so they could resist the discouragement that often comes with this phase of development.

Finally, WRAP took hold and became a recognizable entity in our community culture. The buzz about WRAP was on the airways. Other clinic sites started asking us to do the classes in their sites too, and we were happy to. It wasn't long before our community reached a tipping point, where more people knew about WRAP than didn't, and WRAP became part of our culture. Today we teach over 300 WRAP sessions a month throughout our community. We have also taught it in the Arizona State Hospital, and have trained facilitators to teach there too. WRAP has been a wonderful tool for people to learn to manage their own symptoms and gain the courage to become self-determining. 🕭

7

The Development of Recovery and WRAP in the United Kingdom

Piers Allott

Background

I have been working in and around services for people diagnosed with mental illness since 1966. I have never been comfortable with many of the approaches to people's distress that I witnessed, and for many years searched for better approaches. Eventually I found WRAP.

It was my contact with the Center for Community Change through Housing and Supports and Dr Paul Carling in the mid 1990's that led me to WRAP. However, it was a number of years after first hearing about it that I became fully aware of the Recovery and WRAP facilitators training and trainers manual.

Recovery as a concept in the United Kingdom was difficult to promote, but it was the West Midlands Regional Health Authority that enabled the introduction of the concept through the publication of a series of five Directional Papers. These papers had recovery at their heart, though they did not directly promote WRAP. They did raise awareness within a very traditional English establishment that recovery is possible. It was this that enabled the funding of a Recovery Research Project in September 2000 that had three strands: 1) Training as a Recovery and WRAP Facilitator with Mary Ellen Copeland in Vermont; 2) The development of a recovery literature review; and 3) a small pilot recovery narrative research project. Of these, it was the Recovery and WRAP Facilitators training and Literature Review that have contributed most greatly to the implementation of WRAP in England and the United Kingdom.

Recovery and WRAP Facilitators Training

In order to join this training, it was a prerequisite that I complete Mary Ellen's correspondence course. This was a challenge for me, but one that I took very seriously, spending a lot of time exploring Wellness Tools that would work for me. I was able to use my learning from the work at Anam Cara, a peer operated crisis alternative to hospital admission, to supplement my learning from Mary Ellen's books.

I joined the training in November 2000, along with about 12 people from across the United States, with some from as far away as Texas and Ohio and others from more local States such as Vermont and Massachusetts. It became clear to me that many of these 'consumers' were also mental health professionals, and those who were not appeared to have the support of their local groups, with expectations that they would put their learning into practice once the training was complete.

I found the training challenging but stimulating and benefited enormously from the experience. I learned a lot about recovery and WRAP and experienced considerable anxiety about having to deliver a presentation to the rest of the participants. However, the experience was essential to my development as a Recovery and WRAP Educator.

Literature Review

The literature review was completed in January 2002 and its intention was to promote recovery across the country. It was not published in the normal manner, but was published on the web and through the West Midlands Recovery Network that was established to disseminate information on mental health recovery as a result of the first Recovery and WRAP training in January 2001. The paper states:

The principal author trained as a mental health recovery educator with Mary Ellen Copeland in the US in November 2000 and delivered the first two-day Wellness Recovery Action Plan (WRAP) training in January 2001. This training was so successful that it led to calls, particularly from service users and family members, for ways of disseminating the information, and led to the establishment of the Recovery Network within the West Midlands.

This paper summarized WRAP under the heading of 'Implementing Recovery Oriented Practice' and was the first wide dissemination of Recovery and Wellness Recovery Action Planning knowledge in England.

Delivering WRAP Training in England

Before I left for the Recovery and WRAP Facilitators training in November I had advertised a two-day training in January 2001. At the time I had no idea if there would be any response, and had not expected the overwhelming response we received. I had also arranged for a co-facilitator. We had 37 people on that first training and it was one of the most tiring trainings I have ever delivered. However, it was also the most extraordinary and rewarding.

An African Caribbean mother and her daughter attended the training and at the end of the first day said that this knowledge had to be disseminated because it is so important and more or less demanded that I find a way of doing this. Overnight I came to the conclusion that we had to establish a network of people in recovery in the West Midlands. I put this to the participants on the second day and twenty-two signed up for the Mental Health Recovery Network – West Midlands.

The networks aims were to:

Promote the recovery vision locally & regionally

Facilitate the development & strengthen locally based recovery cells and groups

Promote examples of best practice from regional work

Increase awareness of 'expert patient' self-management and access to training, including WRAP

The Network was formally launched at a conference entitled 'Focus on Recovery' in Birmingham in May 2001. At this time, the Centre was joined by a new administrator, Claire Craven, without whom much of the work of the Network could not have been supported, and the development and dissemination of recovery knowledge and practice would have been curtailed. Claire organized many of the Network events, including conferences and newsletters, as well as the first UK based Recovery and WRAP Facilitators training, delivered in Birmingham in October 2001. She was always at the end of the telephone, and enabled networking in the West Midlands and much further afield as knowledge of recovery and the Network spread. Claire is now studying to be a doctor, with a view to eventually becoming a psychiatrist.

1st UK WRAP Facilitators Training – October 2001

The Network was established as a result of participant requests during the two-day WRAP Training delivered in January 2001. The newly established Adult Learning, Education and Development Centre (LED) decided to support the training of 13 people as Recovery & WRAP Educators, one from each of the Local Implementation Teams in the West Midlands. It was hoped that many of these places would be allocated to people who had their own 'lived experience' of recovery from mental distress and possibly be 'service user' representatives on their local LITs.

The training was delivered by Mary Ellen Copeland and her spouse Ed Anthes, and was also promoted through the Network as an opportunity for members of the Network (and others) to become Mental Health Recovery Educators.

In the end, some 21 people attended this training, although most of these were not nominated, as intended, by the LITs. Of those, it is estimated that six are still active as trainers.

Second UK WRAP Facilitators Training – October 2003

In April 2003, I took up a post as Senior Service Development Fellow at the University of Wolverhampton and was seconded two days per week to NIMHE (National Institute for Mental Health in England). As the Fellow for Recovery, I had a national remit to enable the concept and practice of recovery to begin to become a part of the services being delivered within the National Service Framework for Mental Health (NSF) and as part of the National Health Service Plan for England. Informed by the experience of WRAP within the West Midlands, one of the first tasks was to arrange a further Recovery and WRAP Educators training by Mary Ellen in order to build more training capacity across England.

In a similar way to the previous training, it was intended to engage NIMHE as an organization in taking this work forward, but that proved more difficult since, at that time, the majority of directors and staff were unfamiliar with recovery as a concept and even less familiar with WRAP. It was hoped that each of the NIMHE Development Centers would nominate and fund the training of at least one member of staff and one person with a lived experience of mental illness and/or family members/significant others. In the event, the two DC's in London and Eastern regions did not nominate anyone and two nominated four or more people. Interestingly, the southwest and northeast of England nominated the most participants and it has been in these areas that WRAP has moved forward significantly, but particularly in Devon in the southwest, where a psychiatrist participated in the training.

The Development of Training Trainers in the UK

Following the 2003 training, Mary Ellen indicated that it was unlikely that she would manage to deliver further Recovery and WRAP Educators trainings in the UK. She told me that as I had completed my own personal training and assisted in the delivery of two further trainings, that I should consider training others.

I continued to deliver many two-day trainings, and initially felt unsure of delivering trainings for trainers. In addition, there still was very little support from organizations and funders, although where trainings had been delivered and some understanding of the work begun, interest grew. From April 2004, hosting arrangements for the Recovery Fellow transferred from the National Office to NIMHE East Midlands and the Director there supported the development of recovery and WRAP across the region. She worked to engage the Chief Executives of the five mental health provider organizations. This eventually led to the funding of a training for trainers in February/March 2005.

This five day residential training was held at the Losehill Hotel on the Losehill side of the Valley of Hope, Derbyshire. The training was attended by eighteen people, of whom eight identified as people who had a lived experience, two as family members, and eight as staff. I led the training and was supported by two co-facilitators from the 2003 training. It was a special experience for all participants. However, it is estimated that only half of the group are currently active as trainers, though many of the others now promote recovery and WRAP. Often, trained people in England have difficulty getting the funding or support to deliver further trainings, and for staff members that may mean not being allowed the time from their ordinary positions to deliver trainings. This is not only true of WRAP, but other approaches and interventions as well.

Since March 2005, two more Recovery and WRAP Facilitators trainings have been delivered, in October 2005 in Bedford and in June 2006 in Sleaford, Lincolnshire. The latter training is part of a now more integrated plan to take recovery forward in the East Midlands region and two further trainings are planned.

Outcomes and Evaluations

There can be no better way to begin this section but with a quote from the newsletter that was produced following the Celebration of Recovery, Self Management and WRAP event held in Devon in February 2005 and organized by Partnerships for Mental Health Recovery, a collective of like minded people in Devon. The Newsletter opens with:

"Since Mary Ellen Copeland came to Devon in October 2003,

WRAP (Wellness Recovery Action Plan) has had a life of its own. As a framework or tool to help people stay well and plan their recovery, WRAP has taken the local mental health community by storm. Some ideas need cultivating and nurturing, but WRAP has just taken off and spread all over the county. This is because it is common sense, reflects the way most of us manage our lives and provides a way of taking more active control of our lives.

"The last year has seen an incredible cascading of training in WRAP and spreading of recovery ideas across the local mental health community. This day was a celebration of that fact, a chance to take stock and a chance to look forward. A really good day was had by all."

Of particular interest to me at this meeting was a statement from a senior member of staff from a PCT (Primary Care Trust) that she had used WRAP to reduce her absence from work due to being ill, from three times a year to once a year. She also highlighted that other senior managers wanted to attend WRAP trainings for their own personal benefit. This was a shift that caused me most surprise, given the continuing resistances elsewhere in the country – but was not unexpected since students on the University of Wolverhampton Recovery Module reported that, 'This is an approach we can use for ourselves, not just one that will be helpful for the people with whom we work."

That work has continued in Devon and they are now at the forefront of services in implementing the national STR (Support Time and Recovery) workers, all of whom have had the same training that includes recovery and WRAP. To quote their most recent newsletter:

"STR has developed from being a job description into a way of working. They have in common a shared value system and approach to people based around WRAP and self-management. They focus on social inclusion and recovery, through supporting people to find what keeps them well, what wellness tools they may need to develop to sustain wellness, and practical support during times of distress."

South Tyneside Evaluation

Two of the participants on the 2003 training delivered by Mary Ellen secured funding from their NIMHE Development Centre to deliver a training that had the benefit of being evaluated, although the report of that evaluation has yet to be published. Some of the comments made by participants included:

"The description seemed to be very much in line with a model we would use rather then a purely medical model."

"I think it's important because it instills hope."

"The whole top and bottom of it was to help people to help themselves."

"If this had been in place years ago when I got taken in to the inpatient unit and sectioned because I was sitting in the car down at the beach… if I had a WRAP plan then, they would have realized 'Well, she does this, this is her safe place.'"

"The WRAP tool itself is an absolutely brilliant, brilliant thing."

Conclusion

It is clear that where there has been a commitment to training and supporting people to learn about mental health recovery and WRAP, significant change and personal transformations have occurred. However, we still do not have sufficient commitment for a widespread adoption of WRAP in England. Further robust evaluations are needed to convince our still skeptical traditional mental health professionals.

Perhaps the publication of the two-day recovery training program by the NIMHE National Changing Workforce Programme, as part of the 10 Essential Shared Capabilities training program identified as necessary for the whole of the mental health workforce, will finally bring about this change.

Even without this, people who use mental health services are finding their own way, and, quietly, there is a revolution taking place that is a revolution for the people who matter – those who experience mental distress and their families. WRAP works! ❧

8
Sefton Recovery Group
Experience and Vision

Karen Colligan, *for and on behalf of Sefton Recovery Group Network, Merseyside, England with the support of Piers Allott; from the outset and throughout; National Fellow for Recovery, Care Services Improvement Partnership, England. This piece describes the development of Sefton Recovery Group, its vision and its current activities and its goals for the future.*

Sefton Recovery Group is a group of 'Experts by Experience', an intentional peer-governed network of 350 people deemed to be experiencing "serious and enduring mental illness," people with lived experience of mental illness services, their family and friends, all of whom practice Wellness Recovery Action Planning (WRAP). Being network-centric is all about emotional security, democracy, flexibility and information sharing.

We believe that recovery is the vision for the future of mental health services, accelerating a shift away from a total focus on illness, toward creating and maintaining mental well being. A recovery approach provides everyone with an opportunity to take back control over their life, whether in the presence or absence of illness, through self-management approaches such as WRAP. This is part of a larger paradigmatic shift across the Western world in constructing healing contexts for individuals, organizations and community.

Beginnings

We came out of "user only" spaces and self financed the North West Consumer Network over the last thirty years. There is a strong human rights and independent mental health advocacy ethos in our approach and we have cross-party political support for our work.

In the spring of 2002 the group found a paper on the Internet entitled: 'Discovering Hope for Recovery from a British Perspective' (Allott, P. et al 2002). We found this paper inspirational and we decided to organize a conference, Focus on Recovery. One hundred members participated at that 2002 conference and this signaled a significant change to our operations in Sefton.

We followed this in December of the same year with the first public showing in the United Kingdom of Mary Ellen Copeland's Wellness Toolbox and Wellness Recovery Action Plan videos, which were played on the big screen at our local cinema.

The group then decided to commission a two-day Mental Health Recovery and WRAP Education program facilitated by Piers Allot, now National Fellow for Recovery in England. Twenty-one "Experts by Experience" participated, including a local councilor, a Eucharistic minister, a manager of a large residential home for older people, a complementary therapist, a manager in further education, and a professional musician. This training enabled members to equip themselves with the tools to self manage their own mental well being, and increased their enthusiasm to awaken others to Recovery as the vision for the future of mental health (meaning health) services.

A series of meetings were held over the course of a week in May 2003 at a Recovery Respite Centre, based in a Quaker Meeting House in mid Wales. 'A Pursuit of Risk' was the theme of the meetings, which included discussion of testing unproven ideas, intangibles based on our instincts, vigor to invent new ways of working and change language. This inspired courage to deal with the power issues associated with pursuits of 'positive risk', drawing on wisdom gained over a quarter of a century in the frontline of user engagement (not user involvement).

Recovery is a process which recognizes and acknowledges the tricks of discrimination-sidelining, subjugating and silencing; and the very real attempts at character assassination led by those and theirs who belong to the old ways of working. We'd been at a pivotal point of change before; and we'd got through it against adversity. 'Resilience' is our strength.

Supporters

Our group has continued to grow and develop its ideas. Successful cross platform collaboration with Southport and Waterloo Colleges of Further Education and Liverpool City Community College have borne fruit in a range of programs headed Wellness Toolbox sessions: complementary therapies, guitar keyboard and midi-recording, craftwork, T'ai Chi, journaling, creative writing recovery narratives; etc.

Lessons learned

We have learned that by practicing certain wellness tool disciplines, confirmation in the light of painful experiences may be seen as meaningful and creative. What use is a session once or twice a week (people may ask) when you have to get on with your life in between? What these sessions provide are some powerful tools, which become our regular practice and our daily experience, to incorporate in the flow of life.

Coupled with a structured rolling program of Mental Health Recovery and WRAP education, life becomes less of a struggle. We have found that most people delve into one wellness tool, and stick with it for an extended period of time in order to experience the healing and transformative effects of the tool, before adding more to their toolbox. We have learned Recovery takes effort by all parties, especially the person experiencing distress/illness.

Key obstacles in getting to what really needs to be changed

A key barrier has been the behavior of some people, particularly in statutory services, who don't get it and yet retort; "But we're already doing it" … Doing what? Equipping people to self-manage their lives? In the presence or absence of a deemed serious and enduring mental illness?

Another is the distribution of wealth investment in mental illness services, a real barometer of stigma and discrimination which is rife. In any one Primary Care Trust footprint there is probably less than 0.05% of total 'mental illness' money spent on intentional, peer-governed, peer-operated services. SHIFT that.

We also need to accelerate research to promote recovery and decrease the prevalence of 'mental illness' through rapid feedback loops reporting research findings of what helps and what hinders peoples' recovery real time.

Finally, a belief that mental health systems have the ability to offer services that are helpful to a person's recovery is important. Where this is not thought to be the case, a belief that systems can recover is essential.

Commissioning

We have further invested in expanding our portfolio by exploring and applying Mental Health Recovery Education and WRAP to the local commissioning cycle using visioning exercises. (The commissioning cycle describes the main stages of the commissioning process and tasks to be addressed within each stage of the strategic framework: planning, purchasing of services, monitoring and review.) Participants gather in a circle and a challenge is posed: We have been successful in achieving our Recovery vision. What does it look like? What are its attributes? How did we get here? Finish the exercise when it feels participants have expressed all attributes, and pathways to their Recovery Vision.

The Vision

Self-agency is a new way of life here, as people educate themselves and others about Mental Health Recovery and WRAP. We have all worked together to make Recovery the expected outcome. Our vision is secure through educating all Sefton citizens (in the presence or absence of illness) in self-management approaches such as WRAP.

Future Plans

But how serious are we? We are already committed to offering an entirely self financed, twice weekly Wellness Toolbox and Mental Health Recovery and WRAP training program to people with a deemed serious and enduring mental illness in Sefton.

We have formally put the following question (supported by a petition signed by the people of Sefton) to our Health and Overview Scrutiny Committee, who from January 2003 has had a responsibility to scrutinize local health services (Health and Social Care Act 2001).

This new function will look not only at National Health Service (NHS) services, but also at health inequalities and health improvement, with the aim of enhancing health and well being locally. Local Authority Overview and Scrutiny Committees will now also be consulted by the NHS on substantial service variations and can refer contested decisions to the Secretary of State for Health.

'What percentage of total mental illness spending goes to 'Intentional Peer Governed Peer Support Services?'

One of our major development priorities for the future will be a speculative, demand led, investment program in Recovery literature. Our first publication has been an anglicized version of Wellness Recovery Action Plan, authored by Mary Ellen Copeland and edited by Piers Allott; (ISBN 0 9549295 0 0 January 2005). Income from WRAP book sales go to pay the rent at our centre for Wellness Tools in Sefton.

Tying all the strands together

Recovery practice values the role hope plays in the recovery of individuals, organizations and community. A vision of a Recovery world (coupled with a game fixing coalition that recognizes stigma and discrimination), sets a transformational anchor to accelerate a transfer of opportunity away from old ways of working, toward healing systems liberated to self direct and explore every contextual opportunity for Wellness Recovery Action Planning. ❧

9

The Power of WRAP as a Transformative Recovery Tool within Community Mental Health Settings

Ontario, Canada

Ann Thompson

Over the past two years, following my certification as a WRAP Facilitator at one of Mary Ellen Copeland's Brattleboro, Vermont week-long workshops, I have focused my energies on introducing WRAP within a variety of community mental health settings in Toronto, Ontario, Canada. As part of my contribution to this book I want to share with you the power of WRAP as a transformative recovery tool. Starting with a pilot recovery project in a small case management agency, the positive experience from this project has ultimately led to requests for WRAP programs in another much larger case management agency, a supported housing agency, a consumer/survivor initiative, a family support agency, and a supported employment/education program connected with case management services. In effect, Toronto now has the nucleus of a network of recovery-based services within a major Canadian city, despite the fact that the overall provincial/national mental health system follows a predominantly traditional medical model. WRAP is providing a much-needed tool to transform mental health services to a recovery orientation, from the grassroots upwards.

The first WRAP group conducted in Toronto was in a small case management agency called Alternatives, in June 2004. True to its name, this agency was actually the first community mental health service in the city to decide to offer an alternative to traditional case management services, namely a survivor-run self-help group program grounded in mental health recovery values. Three WRAP groups, each eight weeks in duration, were run over the fall and spring of 2005. Participants who expressed an interest in learning to facilitate WRAP were offered opportunities to "shadow" in a subsequent WRAP group. Depending on their comfort level, they were encouraged to lead discussions and record brainstorming sessions on easel pad paper, among other things.

As part of the closure process for each WRAP group, participants were asked if they would like to continue meeting on a regular basis. The majority said yes, so a weekly Peer Support program was introduced. In an effort to integrate WRAP values within this new Peer Support group, it started with an initial six work session based on the Copeland & Mead workbook, *Wellness Recovery Action Plan & Peer Support: Personal, Group and Program Development.*

Reflecting back on this year-long process of introducing recovery programs at Alternatives, it is interesting to note that when WRAP participants were asked which program they would have chosen to attend first, they all indicated that WRAP was their number one choice – if Alternatives had offered Peer Support initially, they said they would not have come out. It was only following their very positive group experience with WRAP that their attitudes and interests changed toward peer support. A number of folks mentioned that their previous experiences with peer support groups had mostly been negative because these groups seemed to be dominated by illness and problem-laden conversations. In addition, another recent positive development at Alternatives has been a series of workshops organized by one of the WRAP graduates – topics are wellness and recovery-oriented.

The next agency to seriously consider implementing mental health recovery principles was a large supported housing agency called House-link (with over 400 members and 55 plus staff). Over the course of 2005, they asked me to lead three WRAP groups in several of their apartment complexes. Simultaneously, I conducted three 12-week recovery education series for all their front-line housing workers and management. A Recovery Workgroup of over 50 members and staff has evolved from both the WRAP and staff training process. This Workgroup's task is to provide leadership in integrating recovery values throughout all House-link policies and programs.

Some interesting developments to date have included the decision to hire a Recovery Wellness Worker (rather than another housing sup-port staff) from amongst their own members, who will help initiate re-covery programs, like WRAP and Peer Support, within all their hous-ing units. Workshops on nutrition, exercise, and healthy weight loss are being planned, as well as "knowing your medications' side effects". They have set up a Recovery Resource Centre for members and staff, and plan to provide content for a new Wellness/Recovery section created in their regular newsletter to members.

A second case management agency, Community Resource Connec-tions of Toronto (CRCT) decided to follow Alternatives' direction and asked me to introduce WRAP groups in three of their locations across the city. One group was designated "Women Only", as part of a home-less women's project, and another was offered to a predominantly Asian population in Eastern Toronto. A Peer Support group has recently been initiated, as well as a regular speaker series on wellness topics selected and facilitated by their own clients.

In May 2005 the Krasman Centre, a unique consumer/survivor initiative (CSI) located just north of Toronto in Richmond Hill, made the commitment to have their staff of five and all their Board members be introduced to the WRAP program. Early in 2006 I returned there to conduct a WRAP Facilitator Training Workshop. Now the Krasman Centre is not only scheduling WRAP sessions at their own premises, but they are also receiving requests to run WRAP groups at local community mental health centers and supported housing facilities in the area.

The Krasman Centre is presently creating a Recovery Resource library of articles, books and videos, and has plans to offer recovery-based Peer Support and WRAP training to other consumer/survivor initiatives in the near future. What also makes the Krasman Centre quite unique and a wonderful role model for other CSIs is that they also offer a family mental health recovery education series and ongoing support for families as well. They are truly recovery-based in every sense of the word.

Not long after I began to facilitate WRAP groups in the agencies mentioned above, I was hired by the Family Outreach & Response Program (FOR), a small family support agency in Toronto, as their first Family Recovery Resource Worker. My primary task is to develop curriculum and training for mental health recovery education in a family setting. This education is mainly for families dealing with mental health challenges, as well as family support workers and other mental health providers. The current 8-week recovery education series has one session devoted entirely to Self-Care and it's here that we introduce families to WRAP. They are especially encouraged to take information about crisis planning to their family members and to support their choices wherever possible. This Fall, as a pilot project, we are planning to offer a WRAP series for families coming for their own individual support, as well as a workshop on WRAP planning for families as a unit.

The final agency where WRAP has been instrumental in bringing recovery values to service delivery is a supported employment/education program, called WIN (Work Initiatives Network), located within a small case management agency. I will facilitate four WRAP groups, each 8 weeks in duration, which consumer/survivors from five partner agencies can use as a preparation for their entry into the WIN job counseling and placement program. The primary goal of these sessions is to offer consumer/survivors, who are contemplating a return to school or work, an opportunity to engage socially in group discussions, immerse themselves in a safe learning environment and, most importantly, learn relaxation techniques and coping strategies to deal with anxiety and employment related issues.

To date feedback has been very positive – WRAP graduates say they are better prepared and feel more comfortable going into job counseling sessions. The WIN providers report a noticeable difference in their confidence and readiness to engage in back to work/school planning.

In summary, from my own perspective, I believe the WRAP groups have provided a "kick start" to the recovery process within these various community mental health settings. On an individual level, WRAP appears to be helping folks get "unstuck" and swinging the focus onto their own personal wellness. Each group has been unique in its very own way and has created numerous opportunities for "case managers" to observe their "clients" grow in ways they hadn't previously believed possible. Indeed, WRAP is proving to be a very effective catalyst for recovery-based change in a variety of community mental health settings. ❧

Where Do We Go from Here?

So there you have it. Lots and lots and lots of stories about WRAP. Let me remind you that this book is not all-inclusive. There are hundreds of thousands of stories about WRAP out there, being told in other formats, or waiting to be told. I hope this book has convinced you, or further convinced you, of the power of this simple tool, designed and developed by those of us who experience mental health difficulties.

Maybe you have read this book from cover to cover. Maybe you have just read selected parts. In any case, you now know a lot about WRAP. You may be asking, "What does the future hold for WRAP and Mental Health Recovery?"

Every day and every year, the interest in, support for, and adoption of mental health recovery and WRAP key concepts and methods grows and grows and grows, in the United States and around the world. WRAP is reaching out to new constituencies, like veterans and people in the military, those with addictive disorders, families, children, students, and people with other kinds of life challenges, like learning disabilities. Resources are being translated into languages like French, Spanish, Japanese, Chinese and Maori. I continue to be astounded at how the word spreads, without big grants, corporate funding or government funding (although they like us very much), mostly by word of mouth, assisted by the Copeland Center, and through our resources, newsletter and website, mentalhealthrecovery.com.

There is no turning back. This work, along with the spectacular work of many brilliant, recovery-focused people, has taken over the mental health field. While there may be times when it feels like things are sliding back to the old ways, too much has happened, too much has been accomplished, to ever revert to the oppressive and repressive ways of the past. It is like the story of the hundredth monkey. One monkey found that the sweet potatoes they ate were tastier when she first washed the sand off. Another monkey noticed what she was doing, tried it and liked it, and started doing it, too. Other monkeys, observing their behavior, tried it, liked it and began doing it as well. Soon 99 monkeys were doing it. When the hundredth monkey started doing it, all the monkeys began doing it and the old ways were forgotten. That is how I like to feel about mental health recovery and WRAP. We have hit the hundredth monkey and everyone is doing it. There is no turning back.

Here's what is especially exciting to me. People who used to call the crisis line or get admitted to the hospital when they starting feeling those scary feelings that let them know they might be in for a bout of depression, intrusive voices, or bizarre thoughts and behavior, are now taking action, on their own or with the help of their supporters, that turns things around before it gets out of control, before they need to ask for "professional" help, use invasive treatments or spend time in an institution. They are finding that using their Wellness Tools, doing things like listening to certain kinds of music, watching funny videos, talking non-stop to a friend for a specified length, getting deeply involved in a hobby or walking, walking, walking, really helps. Sometimes they have to use these tools for many days. They have found that it is well worth it.

Many people, like me, have "WRAPPED" their lives around these tools. It has become a new way of living — a way of life that is healthy, rich and rewarding. I once was a frequent guest at the psychiatric hospitals. Care providers knew me. I lived in housing for the elderly at 45 because I was considered permanently disabled. I remember how happy I was to get disability checks so I didn't have to ask my family for help with my expenses.

Now, over 20 years later, my life is very different. I have a wonderful career and accomplishments I am proud of. I have achieved things that have been of great benefit to others. I have a warm and loving spouse. I can cover my own expenses and more. Sometimes I can help out my children, who used to try and figure out how they could support me. My life is filled with activities I enjoy. Every day for me is a "WRAP" day.

However, not everyone in the mental health system has adopted these new ways, based on the key concepts of hope, personal responsibility, education, self advocacy and support; and that adhere to the Mental Health Recovery and WRAP Values and Ethics as I described them in the second chapter of this book. There are still many, many places where these ideas are foreign. Yesterday I got a call that reminded me that we still have a long way to go.

What can we all do to insure that more and more people, mental health agencies, facilities and organizations know about and use mental health recovery and WRAP to benefit everyone?

If you haven't already, take a basic WRAP training course. There may be one in your community. Contact your local mental health agency or peer support group to find out. If there is not one you can attend, you can learn about Mental Health Recovery and WRAP through the WRAP Correspondence Course, an e-learning course on-line, an experienced friend, or by reviewing one or more of the many resources that describe mental health recovery and WRAP.

Sometimes people like to take the course several times and continue to learn about WRAP and Mental Health Recovery in other ways. Work with it and make it a way of life for you. Then tell people how it has helped you, how it has changed your life. Let them know how they can learn about it.

As you become experienced in using WRAP, you may want to support others as they learn about WRAP and integrate it into their lives. This is a great gift to give.

Consider becoming a WRAP group facilitator. Once you have received the training, you can lead WRAP groups and workshops. With more experience, you can take the training to learn how to guide people through the process of becoming a WRAP group facilitator.

Over time, and as you live WRAP, you will discover that there are many other ways you can spread the word about WRAP and support others in their recovery and wellness.

—**Mary Ellen Copeland**

Links for Mental Health Recovery and WRAP resources:
mentalhealthrecovery.com/shop/index.php

E-learning courses:
mentalhealthrecovery.com/elearning.php

Correspondence Course and Training:
copelandcenter.com

<u>Self-Help Resources by Mary Ellen Copeland, PhD</u>

<u>The Depression Workbook</u> Second Edition $19.95 x _____

<u>Fibromyalgia and Chronic Myofascial Pain Syndrome: A Survival Manual</u> $19.95 x _____

<u>Healing the Trauma of Abuse: A Women's Workbook</u> with Maxine Harris, PhD $24.95 x _____

<u>Living Without Depression and Manic Depression</u> $21.95 x _____

<u>The Loneliness Workbook</u> $16.95 x _____

<u>Recovering from Depression: A Workbook for Teens</u> with Stuart Copans, MD $24.95 x _____

<u>Winning Against Relapse</u> $16.95 x _____

<u>The Worry Control Workbook</u> $16.95 x _____

<u>WRAP: Wellness Recovery Action Plan</u> $10.00 x _____

<u>WRAP: Wellness Recovery Action Plan for People with Dual Diagnosis</u> $10.00 x _____

<u>Plan de Acción para la Recuperación del Bienestar</u> WRAP-Spanish Version $10.00 x _____

WRAP Quantity Pricing: 1-9 copies, $10 each 10-99 copies, $8 each. 100+ copies, $7 each.

<u>WRAP: Wellness Recovery Action Plan for Veterans & People in the Military</u> $6.00 x _____

<u>WRAP: Wellness Recovery Action Plan for Kids</u> $12.00 x _____

<u>WRAP Software</u> Contains both adult and teen versions $19.95 x _____

<u>The WRAP Story</u> $19.95 x_____

<u>WRAP and Peer Support Manual: Personal, Group & Program Development</u> $40.00 x _____

<u>Facilitator Manual: Mental Health Recovery including WRAP</u> $129.00 x _____

<u>Community Links: Pathways to Recovery</u> Program Implementation Manual $70.00 x _____

Video and Audio

<u>Creating Wellness Workshop</u> DVD $60.00 x _____

<u>WRAP</u> DVD $19.95 x _____

<u>WRAP for Veterans and People in the Military</u> DVD $19.95 x _____

<u>Wellness Tools</u> audio CD $19.95 x _____

<u>WRAP: Step-by-Step</u> audio CD $19.95 x _____

Subtotal $_____

Shipping/Handling: $4 for first item, plus $1 for each additional item_____

Total amount due (for resource items and shipping costs) $_____

Name _____ Organization _____

Address_____

City and State _____ Zip _____

Phone_____ E-mail _____

Make checks payable to Mary Ellen Copeland.

( ) MasterCard ( ) Visa Card # _____ Expires _____

3-digit Security code on back of card_____

Mail order to:

Mary Ellen Copeland, PO Box 301, West Dummerston, VT 05357-0301 USA

mentalhealthrecovery.com

Phone 802-425-3660 FAX 802-425-5580

books@mentalhealthrecovery.com